Young W
2004 POETRY CO

CW00405661

ONCE UPON A RHYME

IMAGINATION FOR
A NEW GENERATION

Scotland
Edited by Aimee Vanstone

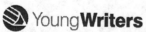 Young**Writers**

First published in Great Britain in 2004 by:
Young Writers
Remus House
Coltsfoot Drive
Peterborough
PE2 9JX
Telephone: 01733 890066
Website: www.youngwriters.co.uk

SB ISBN 1 84460 531 0

Foreword

Young Writers was established in 1991 and has been passionately devoted to the promotion of reading and writing in children and young adults ever since. The quest continues today. Young Writers remains as committed to engendering the fostering of burgeoning poetic and literary talent as ever.

This year's Young Writers competition has proven as vibrant and dynamic as ever and we are delighted to present a showcase of the best poetry from across the UK. Each poem has been carefully selected from a wealth of *Once Upon A Rhyme* entries before ultimately being published in this, our twelfth primary school poetry series.

Once again, we have been supremely impressed by the overall high quality of the entries we have received. The imagination, energy and creativity which has gone into each young writer's entry made choosing the best poems a challenging and often difficult but ultimately hugely rewarding task - the general high standard of the work submitted amply vindicating this opportunity to bring their poetry to a larger appreciative audience.

We sincerely hope you are pleased with our final selection and that you will enjoy *Once Upon A Rhyme Scotland* for many years to come.

Contents

Ziaena Koppernaes (9)	46
Helen Milne (9)	47
Lucy McDonald (9)	47
Christie Duff (9)	47
Neil Kellas (9)	48
Nicholas Simmers (9)	48

Kippen Primary School, Stirling

Rosie Singleton (8)	48
Nicola Kyle (10)	49
Megan Wells (10)	49
Jennifer McNicoll (8)	50
Jennifer Lygate (8)	50
Freya Craig (8)	51
Chloe Arthur (8)	51
Katie McPherson (11)	52
Lauren Hunter (10)	52
Maura Collins (10)	53
Kirsten Thornton (9)	54

Lady Alice Primary School, Greenock

Michaela Magee (10)	54
Laura Gillan (10)	55
Lynsey Nicolson (9)	56
Shareen Lang (11)	57
Christina Wilson (11)	58
Selina Chan (11)	59
Andrew Waddell (11)	60
Kimberley Stevenson (10)	61
Ashleigh Wilson (10)	62
Samantha Barbour (10)	63

Langbank Primary School, Port Glasgow

Murray Clark Anderson (8)	63
Jacqueline Hamilton (9)	64
Mark Baxter (11)	64
Emma Jones (8)	65
Jennifer Mackay (8)	65
Adam Saunders (11)	66
Duncan Fletcher (11)	66

Iain Gillon (9)	67
Gillian Hunter (11)	67
Mark Smith (8)	68
Lindsay Birch (8)	69
Gemma McKenzie (7)	70
Ben Saunders (8)	71
Fern Fletcher (9)	72
Heather McFarlane (7)	72
Ryan Sweeney (9)	73
Holly Fraser (9)	73
Louise Wallwork (9)	74
Sam Campbell (11)	75
Katie Lapping (8)	76

Limerigg Primary School, Falkirk

Chiara Bullen (9)	76
Johnathan Fisher (11)	77
Lisa Rushford (10)	77
Hannah McNeill (10)	78
Megan Risk (11)	78
Nicole McEwan (10)	79
Ross Moffat (11)	79
Kim McLuckie (9)	79
Demi Johnstone (10)	80
Carys Williams (10)	80
Johnathan Beattie (9)	80
Erin Risk (9)	81

Longstone Primary School, Edinburgh

Marc Stables (10)	81
Lauren Anderson (8)	81
Mark Hanlon (9)	82
Leigh McMahon (8)	82
Lauren Notman (10)	83
Zoe McRae (9)	83
Kenny O'Brien (10)	84
Ben Brigg (10)	84
Lisa-Marie Kennedy (11)	85
John Allan (11)	86
Rebecca Scott (10)	86
Laura Small (11)	87

Robbie Jack (9)	87
Natalie Prosser (10)	88
David Wright (10)	88
Elliot Lindsay (11)	88
Emma Kelly (11)	89

Macduff Primary School, Macduff

George Imlach (11)	89
James Milne (11)	90
John Percival (11)	91
Heidi Watt (11)	92
Scott Gillies	92
Sarah Cowie (11)	93
Nicola Hadden (11)	94
Ewan Forbes (11)	95
Ryan West (11)	96

Nethermains Primary School, Denny

Alexander Robertson (10)	96
Steven Jackson	97
Ben McVickers (11)	97
Callum Mincher (9)	98
Andrew Bain (11)	98
David Gordon (11)	99

Pitreavie Primary School, Dunfermline

Josh Dishington (11)	99

Ralston Primary School, Paisley

Kirsten Hamilton (9)	100
Paula Gahagan (9)	100
Calum McLean (9)	100
Gillian Breslin (9)	101
Alasdair Forrest (9)	101
Amy Watters (9)	101
Leigh Baxter (9)	102
Blair Dalgleish (9)	102
Ross Gibson (9)	103
Laura Russell (9)	103
Emma Ross (9)	104

Rashielea Primary School, Erskine

St Andrew's Primary School, Falkirk

Nicola Barclay (9)   136
William Urban (9)   136
Steven Hogg (10)   136
Stephen Fraser (9)   137
Sean Allan (11)   137

Thorn Primary School, Johnstone
William Wylie (11)   138
Stuart McCormick (10)   139
Andrew Smith (11)   140
John Milligan (11)   141
Alan Smith (10)   142
Gary Bull (11)   143

Uplawmoor Primary School, Glasgow
Nichola Philp (11)   143
David Ross Paterson (11)   144
Laura Wood (11)   144
Laura McMurdo (11)   145
Caroline Nicol (11)   145
Jonathan Dawson-Bowman (11)   146
Jessica Strang (10)   146
Isla Erskine (10)   147
Ben Rodger (11)   147
Alison Macleod (11)   148
Angus Erskine (11)   148
Jessica Maycock (11)   148
Joi Dinsmor (10)   149
Gemma Egan (10)   149
Sarah Addie (10)   149
Lucy Morrant (10)   150
Naomi Dawson-Bowman (11)   151

Wallacestone Primary School, Falkirk
Jordan Moir (11)   151
Amy Tucker (12)   152
Daniel Struthers (10)   152
Laura Henderson (12)   153
Jennifer Sneddon (11)   154
Richard Fairgrieve   154

The Poems

My Bed

Cosy, springy bed,
stands strong and bold,
castle walls,
guarding me from the fire-breathing dragon.

Pink patterned bedspread,
tight on the mattress like a snake round its prey.

New puffy pillows,
soft as candyfloss swirling round
and round in the drum.

Peace and quiet, locked away civilisation.

Soft and cuddly teddy sits lonely by itself
a solitary palm tree on a deserted island.

Soothing relaxing mattress, warm and reassuring,
a bubbling Roman spa.

Sink steadily into quicksand and
nod slowly off to sleep.

Kristine King (11)
Arkleston Primary School, Renfrew

My Favourite Place, My Bed

I feel just like a sleeping, contented cat
in front of a warm cosy fire.

I delve among its spongy depths
like a powdery pink marshmallow.

Comfy pillow, absorbent qualities,
a mass of cotton wool.

Soft cuddly quilt, amply padded,
wraps round me like a caterpillar in cocoon.

Broxi asleep on my bed, his usual spot,
keeping it warm until I return.

Deaglan Ovens (11)
Arkleston Primary School, Renfrew

My Bedroom

Brand new carpet,
bubblegum and bluebell coloured,
its thick pile comforts me.
Calming, soft touch.

Tall broad bookcase,
silver handles, brand new buttons,
its books lined up in size order,
beckon me to read.

Soft delicate bed,
lilac as a bed of autumn violets
Smooth, velvety covers,
wrap round me like a bandage
on a complex fracture.

Ancient antique bear collection,
jaded colours, muted tones.
My old favourite, worn-out tatty lamb,
reliant on me for a much-needed hug.

Heavy oak wardrobe,
spray painted silver,
little tints of glitter sparkle in the light.

Metallic CD player,
booming clubland music,
volume to the max
feel safe and alive
can't hear parents - that suits me!

For once the rumble in my tummy
drains the music, mind made up,
time for tea.

Heather W R McPherson (11)
Arkleston Primary School, Renfrew

My Favourite Place, My Bedroom

Huge, heavy cabinet,
oak timber frame stands tall,
unmoveable.

Multicoloured ornamental
Beanie Babies,
taking up space like
an ocean of colour.

Shiny, silver bed
comfy and soft,
awaiting my company.

Hard wooden floorboards,
lumpy and stiff, littered
with sweet wrappers.

Tall, scary mirror
glaring at me with a cold stare.

Angry big brother,
cross-armed, verbal venom,
expression drawn on his face.

Special blue lights,
shining brightly like the sun.

Quiet black TV
no movement, no sound,
blank and vacant.

Old, splintered door
graffiti and squeaky,
lifeless and bare.

Reach for the handle,
open the door . . .
and leave.

Sarah Gunn (11)
Arkleston Primary School, Renfrew

My Room

Swing open pearly white doors
everything perfect
Warm reassuring rug tickles my toes,
reluctant to let me go.

Comforting heat invites me in
time to relax,
slouch down in my sofa bed,
teddies surrounding me,
protecting me from any dangers,
telling me their news.

Sink into its grasp,
hot, comfy, roastie-toastie bed
holds me tightly in its big strong frame
like a bear shields its cub.

Drift away into a light sleep
no sooner than when my head touched
the soft silky pillows.
I was awoken by the sound of oriental
voile curtains dancing in the wind,
laughing as they move.

Smooth modern mirror,
locks my face in its case.
Contented and safe,
a special palace,
my room.

Donna Houston (11)
Arkleston Primary School, Renfrew

My Favourite Place

Bright golden sunlight,
a waxy yellow grapefruit,
gleaming through my window.

Soft beige carpet, silky sand,
blowing slowly across my bedroom floor.

Soft cosy bed,
pink and lilac (irises and dahlias)
on a hot summer's day.

Smooth pine wardrobe
standing tall and broad,
tower block watching over the town.

Shiny silver telly,
sitting patiently on its stand,
bored as Goldie in his bowl.

Flowery cotton curtains,
blowing in the gentle breeze
like leaves being detached
from their branch.

'What's that noise, Mum?'
Time to go to bed.
Shut my window, close curtains
Climb into my cosy bed and soon -
I am fast asleep.

Jaspreet Kainth (11)
Arkleston Primary School, Renfrew

My Tempting Bed

Soft warm bed,
sucking me in like a vacuum cleaner,
pinning me down like twenty American footballers
- almighty pile up!

Tall, arched headboard
towering above,
shielding me from any bad dreams,
no distractions.

Rectangular white pillow,
flexible and squashy,
rubbing softly against my cheeks like the
perfect face massage.

Spring, bouncy mattress,
an acrobatic performance, flipping
and turning on the blue and black trampoline.

Smooth, calming sheets,
cosy and welcoming
like a caterpillar in its cocoon.

Happy and luxurious dreams
tranquil and heavenly,
like sitting in the Mosque, quietly
looking up to the green dome,
translating the patterns.

Comforting tempting quilt
white as white,
fluffy and feathery
like the largest cloud in Heaven.

Arif Nadeem (11)
Arkleston Primary School, Renfrew

My Tropical Island

Hot, deserted, uncharted island,
Isolate, alone,
No interruptions,
Just peace and quiet.

Restful, smooth, golden sand,
I'm relaxed and carefree.

Scorching sun beats steadily,
A great ball of fire,
Hot rays award a healthy glow.

Palm trees sway gently,
Like large, bulky pineapples,
Coconuts wobble dangerously,
Twisting, turning, twisting, turning.

Shells on shore,
Crimson red, fiery orange,
Sunshine yellow, pearly white,
Colours of the rainbow, shells wash away.

White horses gallop to shore,
Hooves thunder by.

Tropical fish rapidly scuttle
Like shooting stars everywhere.
Terrified by the hunting birds.

Ships on horizon,
Sun melts down slowly,
Behind its dividing line.

My favourite place.

Maxine MacDonald (11)
Arkleston Primary School, Renfrew

My Favourite Place

Quiet lonely bedroom,
a place to escape to
until I switch the light on.

As soon as I do my room comes alive.

Teddies afford a welcome nod, a wink and a grin.

Soft bouncy bed, like a trampoline on holiday.
Crazy alarm clock
and its pointy arms, not stopping for a break.

Spooky mirror staring straight back at me,
like a reflection in the water.

Unread dusty bookshelf,
pile upon pile of books
just lying there, taking up space.

Pinball machine, gathering dust aimlessly,
like collecting flowers.

'Lisa, tea's ready!' shouted Mum.
'Oh! Oh! Got to go!'
As soon as I turn the light out
everything goes to sleep.

Lisa Stephen (11)
Arkleston Primary School, Renfrew

My Bedroom

Step into my room, feels safe.

Brand new bed
waiting to comfort me,
a loving loyal teddy bear.

TV welcomes me
loud and proud
it leaps into gear.

Small bears,
clutching onto the curtains,
a mother's comforting hug.

Wicker washing basket
full to the brim,
heaving, wrestling with damp clothes.

Chrome uplighter lamp
stands tall, delivering a bright shining light,
brighter than the waxy yellow sun.

Snuggle-up tight,
clutch my bear,
soon enough I'm fast asleep.

My special place, my bedroom.

Emma Kerr (11)
Arkleston Primary School, Renfrew

My Favourite Place

Cosy springy mattress supporting my body
helping me to sleep comfortably

Fluffy warm pillow
which takes me to the Land Of Nod.

Silky blue quilt, gripping on to me,
not wanting to let go.

Big brown bars make me feel like
a helpless trapped zoo animal.

Small but expensive Burberry hat
hangs out at the other end of my bed.

Big black TV disappointed,
anxiously waiting to be turned on.

Heavy solid weights, gathering dust
but begging to be polished.

Ranger's scarf, wrapped endlessly round
bunk bed bars
like a mysterious desert snake.

Grant Rae (11)
Arkleston Primary School, Renfrew

Bonfire Night On The Beach

Distant fireworks crack loudly upon the pier,
Bonfire becomes greater,
a Caesar in the making,
hulking by the minute,
sparkling Centurions into
the night-time arena.

Gritty sand burrows between my toes,
placid water, peaceful, patient.
Crescent moon,
rocking drowsily in a patchwork starry sky.

Jagged, rugged rock,
closing in as the night grows old.
Deckchairs huddle together
coory up like a babe in arms.

Boats' rudders halt at dusk,
Candles burn, heighten then peter out
even the breeze freezes.
My favourite night of the year.

Rachel J Elliott (11)
Arkleston Primary School, Renfrew

My Bedroom

Ragged torn mat, warm and sea-blue, letting my dog rest.

Worn elderly bed
high above the world, helping me snooze.

Dipping relaxing chair,
creamy and white colours, comforting me as I watch TV.

Silent stingy den, shady with specks of light, protects me
when I need to hide.

Sleeping disengaged TV, dreaming of entertaining me
as programmes come closer.

Alert and aware, my dirty grimy window, patterned with
fingermarks and steam, watches my every move.

In a deep sleep high above, my soft damp curtains,
striped with blue and yellow, remain untouched and undisturbed.

Robbie McAdam (11)
Arkleston Primary School, Renfrew

Favourite Place

Bouncy, springy bed
freshly made and stretched,
calls my name and welcomes me in.

Smooth shiny TV
newly polished, black as night
awaiting my activation.

Ancient, abandoned computer
cornered by posters gathering dust.
Sparkling wooden cabinet
loaded with junk
lies unused, untormented.

Massive multicoloured curtains
not fully drawn, light in my eye
I squint and pull them closer.

Craig Crawford (11)
Arkleston Primary School, Renfrew

Young Writers - Once Upon A Rhyme Scotland

My Favourite Place, My Bedroom

Coal-black television sitting still, bored
like a child peering out on a rainy day.

Blue snugly sheets lie lazily on the bed
waiting to be cuddled during the night.

Wide clear Velux window looks at the weather
as the days go by.

Shiny blue wallpaper glued firmly to the wall,
row after row, column after column.

Grassy green fields overlook a neighbouring village,
a snugly patchwork spread over the landscape.

Blue pine drawers stand tall and proud
overlooking the bedroom.

Clean white bookcase occupying a corner position,
comics, novels, annuals - all gathering dust.

Ross Johnston (11)
Arkleston Primary School, Renfrew

My Favourite Place, My Bedroom

Silver metal headrest, shiny and polished,
smooth beneath my fingers.

Depressed, frustrated, TV redundant,
gathering dust, sneezing on standby
but watching me still.

Tilted Velux window, lying on the roof, open wide,
inhaling and exhaling the fresh air.

Old broken PlayStation, chipped and
shattered, disliking its deep sleep.

Padded soft duvet, warm as my winter parka,
tucking me tightly in.

Alastair McIntosh (11)
Arkleston Primary School, Renfrew

The Beach

Soft sand warms my bare shoulders,
wraps around them like a cosy,
comforting, cotton blanket.

Nimble fingers of the salty sea breeze,
comb my hair, roughly.

Smooth oval pebbles form,
colourful rainbow mosaics in the sand.

Incoming tide gentle
and continuously lapping at the soles of my feet,
reminding me of the way my dog softly licks them.

Rays of golden sun beat down and
heats my entire being
like sips of creamy hot chocolate
on a frosty, winter's night.

Get up, final glance, look around, incoming tide,
untidy shoreline, stagnant rockpools,
tide fast approaching -
time to leave - be back tomorrow.

Julia Povah (11)
Arkleston Primary School, Renfrew

My Favourite My Bed

Firm springy mattress supports my body
encouraging my dreams

Soft, warm pillows cushioning
my head softly

Quilt wrapping me up tightly
like a closed leather wallet

Silver bars caging me
like an animal

Loose green sheets
tangling together
like spaghetti Verde

Black silky goalie strip
beat up badly

Close curtains behind me,
clamber up to my bed
and fall quickly asleep.

Jamie Barlow (11)
Arkleston Primary School, Renfrew

My Bedroom

Warm, soft bed,
comfortable and reassuring,
standing tall at the end of the room.

Sean's low, wide double bed,
mysterious and petrifying,
shadows hitting against the opposite wall.

Sleek, powerful PS2
entertaining and tempting,
towering on its stand.

Gigantic, dominating wardrobe,
huge and on guard,
watching over the sea-blue carpet,
waiting to open the fortress gate.

Sleeping, restless TV
crackling and smooth,
waiting impatiently for a captive audience.

Small, fat drawers,
strong and protective,
letting only a small selection
see what's inside.

Still, cat-like curtains,
eager and ready to pounce,
waiting for the first signs of night-time.

Stupid, blank window,
staring vacantly,
looking at the evening sky above.

Suddenly, the loud and long chorus
of my mum's voice, ringing around the house,
her speech breaks the silence.
'Dinner time!'

Steven Ramage (11)
Arkleston Primary School, Renfrew

My Favourite Place

Resting on bed, computer
screaming, 'Play me! Play me!'

Pick up control,
it's warm to touch.

The computer springs to life at
the flick of a switch.

TV greets me with a lively uproar,
controller vibrates eagerly
shaking my hand.

The game started loading,
loading, seconds away from
duelling with an old friend,
5 . . . 4 . . . 3 . . . 2 . . . 1.

Then Mum's voice comes, croaky
and accusing, agitated and
dangerous, the voice depriving me
of my leisure.
I slowly retreat, the computer
gives a slow wail,
begging me to reconsider
my actions.

Mark Chambers (11)
Arkleston Primary School, Renfrew

What Is The Sea?

The sea for me is . . .
The foaming waves crashing off the rocks like a raging tiger.
The taste of the salty water making my stomach turn,
A mountain of water trying to flood my valley.

The sea for me is . . .
Swimming free like a fish in the sea,
Fish gliding past me with their silky scales brushing my leg.
The deeper I go, the water feels like ice.

The sea for me is . . .
The seaweed smelling like a garbage bin.
The feeling of the bladder rock on my feet, making me shiver.
Watching the seaweed as it dances under the water.

The sea for me is . . .
The seagulls screeching like a violin out of tune,
Their eyes like two little searching stones
Their claws like needles jagging into my arm.

The sea for me is . . .

Jenna Carmichael (11)
Banchory Primary School, Tullibody

The Desolate Domain

As we walked through the desolate domain,
The two little figures screaming with pain,
I wished I had stayed at home in bed,
One more step I'll probably be dead.

As we walked through the desolate domain,
Filled with destruction, with death and with pain.
Nothing for miles but thick black smoke,
One more breath, I'll probably choke.

As we walked through the desolate domain . . .

Sean Barr (9)
Banchory Primary School, Tullibody

The Dragon That Lives In The Dull Domain

The dragon that lives in the dull domain
The cave is so dark you could go insane
When he spreads out his eagle-like wings
He soars through the air as morning springs

The dragon that lives in the dull domain
People he captures are screaming with pain
This dragon is devilishly smart
With one sharp claw he can rip you apart

The dragon that lives in the dull domain
On the wall is a disgusting red bloodstain
He knows when you're around with his sensitive smell
If I should see him I would jump down a well!

The dragon that lives in the dull domain . . .

Nicky Walls (10)
Banchory Primary School, Tullibody

Blood-Red Eyes Sparkle In The Dark Domain

Blood-red eyes sparkle in his dark domain
See the skeletons and the blood-red stains
Sharp stalagmites pierce up through the ground
His smoky snorts are the only sound.

Blood-red eyes sparkle in his dark domain
Ready to strike innocent victims, full of pain
Massive crocodile jaw with daggers for teeth
Stealing bones is the only theft of this thief.

Blood-red eyes sparkle in his dark domain
Watching him eat would drive you insane
Spreading out his bat-like wings
Soaring away as morning springs
Blood-red eyes sparkle in his dark domain . . .

Andrew Nisbet (12)
Banchory Primary School, Tullibody

Dragon In The Dark, Damp Dungeon

The dragon in the dark, damp dungeon
The dragon that will never do your will
This dragon is not here to play
This dragon is here to kill

The dragon in the dark, damp dungeon
The dragon with giant wings
It flies so fast in the sky, so bright
Do not touch the dragon - it really stings!

The dragon in the dark, damp dungeon
The dragon gloats with evil plans
The dragon's fiery breath will cause you pain
Nothing can beat the dragon, not even clans.

The dragon . . . in the dark, damp dungeon.

Abbie Johnson (9)
Banchory Primary School, Tullibody

My Hamster

My hamster is cute and cuddly,
Soft and furry,
He's a fast runner.

He has escaped once
He loves running around
In his ball.

He has a white stripe,
With a light brown body.

He loves to run away,
His name is Speedy.

Lewis Blaney (10)
Beaconhurst School, Stirling

Canoe Race

It's my turn
Away I go,
This way and that,
White water rapids,
Never flat.

Up and down,
'Watch that rock!'
People cheering,
Clocks go tick-tock.

Faster I go,
See me fly,
In and out,
My, oh my!

I think I've won,
Well fancy that!
I wake up and it's only my dream
And the dripping bathroom tap!

Carol-Ann McCorgray (10)
Beaconhurst School, Stirling

A Swimming Race

It's really scary at first, standing on the diving blocks,
Waiting for the whistle to blow, go-go-go!
Swim as fast as you can, kick those legs as hard as you can.
Yes, you've won!
As you get out of the water and look up at the crowd
You hear them roaring,
It is a great moment!

Jonathan Priestly (10)
Beaconhurst School, Stirling

Shopping

I love to go on a shopping spree,
Buying things, all for me!
Lots of cool clothes I get to see
Without shopping there wouldn't be a me!

Shopping is really fun,
It's only a pain for my mum!
But I always hear a rumble in my tum,
So I have to chew on a nice fruit gum!

Going into cool clothes shops,
Trying on lots of different tops.
Hearing the music from Top Of The Pops,
Cleaners singing into their mops!

Queuing up outside Millie's to get some cookies,
Walking straight past the bookies!
Going to see the new shop run by my friend Sookie,
There's lots of things to touch and lookie.

Spend, spend all the time,
Why do they never spend on a nursery rhyme?
Seeing the clown's stupid mime,
But all the kids think it's fine!

Now I have to buy a new comb,
Making sure I have enough money for the bus home.
Straight past the shopping centre's garden gnome,
That was a fun day out, shopping in Rome!

Kirsty McDermott (10)
Beaconhurst School, Stirling

The Zoo

First we went to the tigers and we saw them roar,
Then we went to the butterflies but it really was a bore.
Next, we went to the wasp room and we saw some buzzing bees,
We went to see the monkeys, swinging on some trees.

Now we can see a parrot that is talking nonsense all day,
All people say, when they see it, is 'I say!
That bird is trying to talk to us.
Do you think it wants some food?'
So they give it some crackers and cheese
But it just says, 'Don't be so rude!'

The elephants are just lazing around
Giving themselves a bath.
They're filling their trunks with water
And squirting at the staff!

Now it's closing time, we really have to go
But it's so good here, I think I'll come back tomorrow!

Verity Beckham (10)
Beaconhurst School, Stirling

Knights

Knights were born to fight
Some were small, tall and of course, not very bright
All they ever did was fight!
With sword and horses, jousting for fun
Dying dramatically, that sounds like fun!
Not really, it sounds a bit weird!
Now armour was the hip-hop of the years
Their coat of arms on their shield
But all they ever did, was fight!

Tom Westland (10)
Beaconhurst School, Stirling

Teachers

Teachers can be good,
And teachers can be bad.
But my favourite kind of teachers
Are the one's that make me glad!

If I were a teacher
Teaching kids PE,
I'd lay out some mats,
All the kids would jump on them
And then do acrobats!

Some teachers are monsters,
That scream, their faces bright red.
If I ever had one like that
I would just stay in bed!

Some teachers are very nice,
Whom I dream of every night.
She'd have a lovely smile
And her eyes would be so bright.

Music teachers can sing,
And drama teachers can act.
Art teachers can draw
But PE teachers can bat!

David Currie (10)
Beaconhurst School, Stirling

Travelling

When I travel there are ways I like and ways I don't like,
My favourite sporty way is by bike.
When I go by plane,
I always, always complain.
Car is okay, but I sometimes feel sick!
The train is in the middle.

I like to sail as long as it's not bumpy,
All the bus seats are always lumpy.
Skiing is fun but it's only sort-of travelling.
Windsurfing is cool
When you're going to sail.

Zooming everywhere,
Here and there, everywhere.
Travelling is okay.
Games can be fun on the plane,
Sometimes there's a video
In the car Game Boys are handy.
Zooming everywhere, here and there,
That's my point on travelling.

Amy MacKenzie (10)
Beaconhurst School, Stirling

Our Solar System

Our solar system is like a busy classroom.

Mercury. Teacher's pet,
Everything's about the teacher, teacher, teacher.
It's so boring, she never shuts up about her . . .
'Oh, she's soo pretty, I love homework!'
Blah! Blah! Blah!

Venus. She has lots of friends
But don't get on her bad side.
She screams and shouts for the least little thing,
It's so annoying!

Earth. The day dreamer,
She's quite silly and never listens. Always looking at the stars
She thinks she's so cute
With her lacy little clouds and wishy-washy water.

Mars. Thinks he's so hard with his big volcano and fiery redness.
Everyone thinks he's jealous of Earth. I don't know why,
She's just a silly girl!

Jupiter. The fat, clumsy one,
Always dropping stuff and bumping into stars.
The Great Red Spot is an eyesore.
You can't take your eyes off it!

Saturn. The sporty one with her hula hoops,
Always racing around.
Watch her rings spin round and round, so you get dizzy.
But she's real nice and has lots of friends.

Uranus. The quiet one.
The kind of person who reads in the playground and never joins in.

Neptune. Plain. Always has a cold,
Continually sneezing. But watch out!
She sneezed once and blew away
Half the stars!

Pluto. Lazy. Never does any work,
Sits by himself in the corner. No friends.

Lindsay Hilley (10)
Bothkennar Primary School, Falkirk

Mars' Moan

Why is Earth so special anyway?
Just because it has life? Big deal!
I *used* to have life
But I didn't want it anymore!

Earth brags about her large volcanoes and her fancy rivers.
I have the biggest volcano in the solar system!

They think they can investigate me with their stupid Beagle 2s!
I kicked their pathetic machine
Back to where it came from.

It will be a pleasure to let George Bush build
His little colony of humans on me.
But if they build their town it will be bye-bye to them!

Earth thinks she's so cute,
With her lacy little clouds and her ice-blue seas.

But I am hard
And I won't let her kick me down
I am the Red Planet,
Nobody rules me!

Amy Smallwood (9)
Bothkennar Primary School, Falkirk

Five Heroic Astronauts

Five heroic astronauts found an alien door
One knocked on it and he got zapped!
Then there were four.
Four bold astronauts were chased by a purple bee,
One got stung
Then there were three.
Three plucky astronauts didn't see something blue,
Creep up behind them . . . crunch!
Then there were two.
Two fearless astronauts flew to the sun,
One sizzled like a sausage
Then there was one.
One noble astronaut tried to drink some lava from the sun,
So it burned all of his insides and
Then there were none!

Lee Ramage (11)
Bothkennar Primary School, Falkirk

The Incredible Journey

Into a cold, dark space
Across a cool, gigantic moon
Under the sparkly, silver stars
Against the monstrous, orangy Jupiter
Over an old, rusty satellite
Through a bright yellow galaxy
Past a greasy, pink alien
Between a brown, gassy planet
Upon a freezing, green Neptune
Beyond a deep, dark black hole
After an ugly, red Martian
Beneath a cloudy, blue Earth
Beside a gigantic, hot asteroid
And at last, he reached home
Very puffed out
Dirty and dented.

Christopher Ramage (11)
Bothkennar Primary School, Falkirk

Five Bold Astronauts

Five bold astronauts blasted out of the rocket door
One fell down,
Then there were four.

Four fearless astronauts banged into a tree,
One hurt himself
Then there were three.

Three noble astronauts tried the alien's stew,
One found that it was poisoned
Then there were two.

Two adventurous astronauts jumped to the sun,
One found out it was too hot and got fried
Then there was one.

One heroic astronaut went up to the plane,
He kicked the door and hurt his leg,
Then felt himself to blame.

Shelly McCulloch (10)
Bothkennar Primary School, Falkirk

Saturn

As the crew got nearer and nearer
In their space rocket
They gasped -
So smooth, so shiny
Rings singing and whistling
Different tunes to attract them
Smelling like perfume.

But the perfume was poisonous
And the singing is cackling
For I am beautiful on the outside
But I have a heart of ice on the inside
But this is my hobby.

If you are an astronaut, change direction now,
Or suffer my trap!

Suzanne Culbert (10)
Bothkennar Primary School, Falkirk

The Solar System

The solar system. A busy classroom.
The sun. The teacher who may explode any minute!

Mercury. Teacher's pet,
Always close to the teacher's side.

Venus. Always pale.
Watch out! He might be sick on you!

Earth. A daydreamer,
Always puzzled by the stars.
His only friend, the moon,
The only friend he keeps.

Mars. Always complaining,
So jealous of the Earth.
Everyone calls him the Red Planet
Because he's so angry.

Jupiter. A big, fat clumsy girl,
So greedy.
Blocks the view of those behind her.

Saturn. The girly-girl,
Moves gracefully. With all her hypnotising rings
Spinning round and round.

Uranus. The bookworm.
Never joins in. So dull and lonely but peaceful in a way.

Neptune. Fast as lightning,
She's sporty and fun!
Everyone's her friend.

Pluto. So small,
Everyone bullies her. Just weak and sits at the back of them all.
No one knows her.
No one ever will.

Laura Mallis (11)
Bothkennar Primary School, Falkirk

The Moon's Prayer

Dear God,

I was dreaming last night about being free,
You made me to be free
And now I am a slave
Of the Blue Planet.

I was once cheerful, spinning around,
Minding my own business when I was imprisoned
By Earth's gravitational pull.

I miss gazing at the planets and the sun,
Saturn with her beautiful rings,
Mars and his scorching, red temper.
Arguing with Earth about volcanoes,
Jupiter, roaring gently to calm things down.
I pray for mercy.
Please, please let me go.
I want to spin around the sun again
Just like before.
                    Amen

Scott Alexander (10)
Bothkennar Primary School, Falkirk

Five Brave Astronauts

Five noble astronauts had legs that were sore,
One fainted
Then there were four.

Four fearless astronauts smiling with glee,
One forgot his mask
Then there were three.

Three bold astronauts ate poisonous stew,
One just died,
Then there were two.

Two heroic astronauts were looking at the sun,
One went blind,
Then there was one.

One gallant astronaut had spun
He got dizzy and tripped in a hole,
Then there were none.

Caroline Jane Webster (9)
Bothkennar Primary School, Falkirk

Five Adventurous Astronauts

Five adventurous astronauts went to the rocket door
One forgot his helmet,
Then there were four.

Four heroic astronauts jumping with glee
One fell to the floor,
Then there were three.

Three plucky astronauts doing repairs with glue,
One got stuck on the outside
Then there were two.

Two daring astronauts playing with a lazer gun,
One shot himself in the stomach,
Then there was one.

One courageous astronaut wanted some fun,
He went for a moon walk and never returned,
Then there were none.

Cheryl Wilson (9)
Bothkennar Primary School, Falkirk

Th e Incredible Space Journey

Into a long blanket of nothingness
Across a huge asteroid belt,
Under a rusty, spider-like satellite
Against a sparkling, shiny moon
Over a bulky, colourful UFO.
Through an immense, dark galaxy
Past an ample, shiny planet
Between a planet's golden rings.
Upon a small, lumpy, bumpy planet.
Beyond a spooky black hole.
After a purple, stinky alien,
Beneath a compact, gassy planet.
Beside a colossal, red rocket.
Around a great, weird planet
And at last, the spaceship
 Reached Earth.

Alan Mulgrew (10)
Bothkennar Primary School, Falkirk

The Adventures Of A Man From Blackpool

There once was a man from Blackpool,
Who really was rather a fool,
He ate a raw kipper,
Was sick in his slipper
And then duffed it up with a tool!

That fat little man from Blackpool,
Once saw amazingly a ghoul.
He once saw a zombie,
Who smelled rather pongy
And had a jumper made of wool.

This silly old man from Blackpool,
Wasn't very cool!
Fancied himself as a duke
And became one by fluke!
That silly old man from Blackpool!

David Milligan (10)
Cargilfield School, Edinburgh

The Big Competition

Once upon a time there was a competition,
You were only allowed to enter under one condition.
You did not know what this amazing prize could be,
Knights entered from all over the country.
Knights all dressed up in shining armour,
Not one of them looked like an ordinary farmer.

The promoter explained the rules,
The first challenge was to do with bulls.
The men were put in a field with a bull,
Then they had to die or duel.
The men who killed the bulls and put them on the ground
Would be promoted to the next round.

50 men completed this task
They were all given a flask,
Then they had to fill it with dragon's blood
And then drain half into a pile of mud.
The other half was left on the ground,
The people who did this were in the next round.

Five knights were left, Calum, Frederic, Mark, Cruthing and Dail
The next round involved a pail.
The knights had a pail over their head,
They had to fight until four were dead.
The winner was Cruthing,
He got his prize - absolutely *nothing!*

Ailie Corbett (10)
Cargilfield School, Edinburgh

Fairy Night

As I watch the sky, fairies fly by
Faster and faster, what a disaster!
They make no sound, there must be witches around.
Now fairies are screaming
A great light is beaming.
It is the witch!

Screeching and crawling,
They make for the hole,
Quickly now quickly,
The witch is approaching.

Systems running low,
But as light as snow,
They wait till the danger
Has passed
Then at last . . .

The danger has passed,
At last the witch has gone.
I should go back to sleep
It's nearly dawn . . .

Isabella McMicking (10)
Cargilfield School, Edinburgh

My Friend Fred

My friend's name is Fred,
He has an enormous tummy.
When he goes to bed
He takes a whole bowl of bread!
No wonder he is a concern for Mummy . . .

Fred also had lots of friends round
For his birthday,
So he could get many a pound
And spend it on lots and lots of sweets -
As well as many treats!

Fred's best friend is Ned,
Who is now in a bad mood,
Because Fred never shares any food.

So he blew his top
And left Ned like an angry cop!

Now Fred is alone,
Weighing an extra stone
And his only chummy
Seems to be his tummy!

Wendy Heard (11)
Cargilfield School, Edinburgh

Rugby

One day
We went out to play
And I shouted a resounding 'hooray.'

I was playing rugby
And the wind was cutting into my face
As I ran with lightning pace,
To plant that ball on the ground
With a pound -
Behind the line!
To score that dramatic try!
With an ecstatic cry -
That's the life for me . . .

I also like to take the kick
After I step back with my hand making a flick.
It flies straight through the middle
Making me as happy as a fiddle
Before the whistle goes for our dismissal -
We had won!

Tom Russell (11)
Cargilfield School, Edinburgh

Midday

Midday is the sun's highest point
Midday is the time for rest
Midday is the join between morning and night
Midday is the time I like best!

Midday is the time for eating
Midday is the time for lunch
Midday is the time for playing
Midday is the time I like best!

Midday happens every day
Midday happens 365 days in every year -
But 366 days in every leap year
Midday will never leave us
Midday is the time I like best!

Midday will never be morning
Midday will never be night
Midday lasts only one second
Midday is the time I like best!

Hector Maclean (12)
Cargilfield School, Edinburgh

World War II

Hitler - the dictator
Was a trifle bitter.
He hated all Jews
And his cruelty made headline news.
He boldly went to war
And as the reason Europe tore.

But Winston Churchill didn't like the sight
And was wary of Germany's might.
So he made a famous speech
That the Germans would never reach -
His beloved Britain.

He called his allies Fantastic France and Uniformed USA,
But Germinating Germany and Jumping Japan still had their say
And for many years they managed to stay on the winning side,
But eventually Hitler was beaten
And he decided on suicide -
While the Japanese were forced to Emperor-cide.

Sam Kennerley (11)
Cargilfield School, Edinburgh

Jail Break!

You look upon it in the morning,
It always seems extremely boring.
You go down the corridor dark and long
And wait until the lesson bell 'bong'.
The classroom is a prison cell
And you long for the final bell.
With bars on the window and bolts on the door -
This truly *must* be against the law!

And then one day we had had enough,
We were fed up with being treated like pigs eating from a trough.
Then everyone in every class
Would run down the corridor
Like a stampede down a pass!
Screaming and laughing!
Bang! Crash! Boom!
Free at last -
Away from the past . . .

Francesca Lloyd (11)
Cargilfield School, Edinburgh

Solar System

Going in a rocket
To explore the Universe
Going past Mars and Jupiter
Trying to go the furthest
But running out of fuel
Going back to Earth
Isn't very nice
The end of space travel
The last one in your life.

Callan Sinclair (10)
Cowie Primary School, Stirling

Football

Football is fun
You have to run
It's really good
Just like eating food
When players score
They're happy even more
The fans are happy
When their team wins the game
The other team walks off in shame
After the game the players are tired
They go home in fancy cars
And gaze at the stars
Their wives are happy
To see their stars home.

Jack Walker (10)
Cowie Primary School, Stirling

Colours

Baby blue is a sweet colour
The colour red is a dark colour
Yellow is the colour of the sun
Silver is the colour of the moon and stars.

Elaine Marshall (10)
Cowie Primary School, Stirling

Valentine

I think you're good-looking
I think you're smart
I think there's a place for you
In my heart.

Lucy Campbell (9)
Cowie Primary School, Stirling

A Boy Called Sam

There once was a boy called Sam,
Who tried to run after a tram,
The tram crashed,
The windows smashed
And Sam ran away to his mam.

When Sam stopped feeling dim,
He talked to his brother called Tim.
When Tim told his dad,
He said Sam was bad
And smacked him in front of his sister, Kim.

Sam liked to play lots of tennis,
Even though he was a menace.
He had lots of fun,
Playing in the sun
And went on holiday to Venice.

Jack Paterson (10)
Cowie Primary School, Stirling

Mouse

Oncee there was a little mouse,
His name was Jack,
He tried to run and make tunnels.

Jack is very small and rich,
He has lots of food,
He has a straw bed,
He is always warm.

He looks for things,
He is greedy.

Colin Lumsden (11)
Cowie Primary School, Stirling

Football

Football is good
But sometimes rude
It is fun
But you have to run.

During the game
The players hide their face in shame
When the players score a goal
They are happy.

Lee Miller (10)
Cowie Primary School, Stirling

Down In The Forest At Night

Down in the forest at night
An owl got a terrible fright
When gazing at the stars
And wishing he was in Mars
Fell from the tree from a height.

Siân Jenkins (9)
Ferryhill Primary School, Aberdeen

Teachers

There was an old teacher at school
Who everyone thought was cool
Some folks sniggered
When she forgot her knickers
She felt like a right old fool.

Chloe Notman (9)
Ferryhill Primary School, Aberdeen

Little Miss Polly

There was an old lady called Polly,
Everyone thought she was a dolly.
She floated like a water lily
And folks just thought her plain silly,
Now she's in hospital sucking her lolly.

Morgan Fathi (9)
Ferryhill Primary School, Aberdeen

Taking A Photo Of School

When taking a photo of a school,
She stepped backwards like a fool,
She tripped on the kerb
And got mashed like a herb,
That's the end of that fool.

Matthew Firth (10)
Ferryhill Primary School, Aberdeen

The Snowy Pool

A young boy who thought he was flash
Leapt into the pool with a splash
But he did not know
It was covered in snow
And jumped out in a dash.

Kirsty Anne McGillivray (9)
Ferryhill Primary School, Aberdeen

Once On A Journey To Mars

Once on a journey to Mars
An astronaut studied the stars
He leapt out of his suit
And tried to salute
And ate seven king-size Mars bars.

Matthew Fraser (9)
Ferryhill Primary School, Aberdeen

The Moon

An astronaut went to the moon,
Just a wee bit after noon,
He passed many stars,
But stopped on Mars
And on there, he saw a baboon.

Neil Gill (9)
Ferryhill Primary School, Aberdeen

Man On Mars

Once on a journey to Mars
An astronaut studied the stars
He drove past the moon
And saw a baboon
Who gave him a pack of Mars bars.

Ziaena Koppernaes (9)
Ferryhill Primary School, Aberdeen

The Old Lady's Crash

One day an old lady did crash,
She ran away in a dash.
She came back the next day
What a lot she had to pay,
And now she lives on bangers and mash.

Helen Milne (9)
Ferryhill Primary School, Aberdeen

Mrs Scary Mary

There was once an old lady called Mary
And everyone called her scary
She was quite an old bag
Who liked to smoke fags
And thought she was a little fairy.

Lucy McDonald (9)
Ferryhill Primary School, Aberdeen

The Boy From Japan

There once was a boy from Japan
He lived in a rusty old van
His friends all agreed
That what he would need
Was a brand new caravan.

Christie Duff (9)
Ferryhill Primary School, Aberdeen

The Insane Old Man

An old man was so insane
That he jumped off an enormous crane
He ended up dead
After breaking his head
And he was buried in Spain.

Neil Kellas (9)
Ferryhill Primary School, Aberdeen

Old Gran

There was an old gran
Who had a big van
She could not drive
As she crashed into a man.

Nicholas Simmers (9)
Ferryhill Primary School, Aberdeen

Animals

Animals, animals tear up the street
Big ones, small ones all going to meet
Black ones, brown ones and white,
All going to meet at the park.
Koalas, monkeys, climbing in the bark,
Adults shouting at the crying zookeeper
Who shouts back, 'I'm trying!'
Children laughing, singing and dancing
Following the animals prancing
At last the animals are home
Now we can have a drink at the Dome.

Rosie Singleton (8)
Kippen Primary School, Stirling

My Farm Cat

Muffin is my cat
He's black and white and fat
Muffin loves to play
Every minute of the day
He's a little rude
When he doesn't like his food
He jumps from bale to bale
And likes to swish his tail
Muffin catches shrews and mice
Has them for tea and thinks they're nice
Muffin likes it when the moon comes out
So that he can prowl about
He is a big proud tom cat
Who loves to chase a rat!
When the day is at a close
Muffing goes for a doze.

Nicola Kyle (10)
Kippen Primary School, Stirling

Summer's Gone

When the days are getting colder
And the leaves turn red and brown,
Summer days are getting older
And the leaves come tumbling down.

When the big conkers are falling
And the colours all around are bright,
When the winter wind is calling,
It is such a pretty sight.

All the animals are sleeping
And something's drawing near,
The summer frogs aren't leaping,
For autumn's finally here.

Megan Wells (10)
Kippen Primary School, Stirling

Horses

Horses galloping over the hill,
Brown ones, black ones, white ones too,
If you're on their backs, oh what a thrill,
Down through a muddy patch, oh no shoe.

Now home we must go as quick as we can,
A horse with three shoes is not very good,
Down to the blacksmith's and try to find the man,
To put on a new shoe, I hope he does it good.

Now into the stable and clean her all down,
Get her her supper and a fresh bed of hay,
Tell her good night and not to frown,
We'll soon be back, tomorrow's a new day.

When I arrived at the stable next day,
To go for a ride on my lovely mare,
To my surprise there was nothing but hay,
My horse had gone without a care.

Down to the paddock I went right away,
Looking here and there,
She was galloping all around the way,
Without so much as a care.

Jennifer McNicoll (8)
Kippen Primary School, Stirling

The Acrostic Poem

J ennifer is excellent at maths
E xcellent at helping people
N ice girl
N ever nasty
I ntelligent girl
F antastic
E ntertainer
R eally good at singing.

Jennifer Lygate (8)
Kippen Primary School, Stirling

Seasons

Spring days are usually warm,
Hardly ever are they cold,
Lots and lots of flowers are blooming,
Always there for you to hold.

Hot, hot, hot summer,
Lots of soda drinks,
Children run round and round,
It's lovely everyone thinks.

Autumn leaves are falling, falling,
Into the leaves everyone jumps,
Cold winds are calling, calling,
Crinkle crackle leaves are lovely.

Snow, snow, winter's here,
Run inside for hot chocolate,
Why is it cold? It's so queer,
Run inside and sit by the fire.

All of us love seasons so,
Boys and girls come out to play,
Why do we like it? I don't know,
But we just like it anyway.

Freya Craig (8)
Kippen Primary School, Stirling

The Supermarket

Busy, busy supermarket,
Food inside each box and packet.
Ice cream waiting in the freezer,
The till going 'beep!' beside the keeper.

Children, babies everywhere,
By the sweets they stop and stare.
Hurry up, it's getting late,
Hope my mum's bought something great!

Chloe Arthur (8)
Kippen Primary School, Stirling

Super Baby!

Super baby!
You're the best!
Better than all the rest!

Super baby!
Fighting crime!
But not when it's nap time!

Super baby!
Righting wrongs!
Apart from when his nappy pongs!

Super baby!
In the jungle!
Until his tummy starts to rumble!

Super baby!
Soars into space!
Saving all the human race!

Katie McPherson (11)
Kippen Primary School, Stirling

Seasons

I love the spring
When the lambs run free
And the snowdrops begin to grow

I love the summer
When the sun shines bright
And the seven week holiday starts

I love the autumn
When all the leaves fall
And the colours make you feel warm

I love the winter
When the cold winds blow
And the year is coming to an end.

Lauren Hunter (10)
Kippen Primary School, Stirling

The Creature From The Black Lagoon

The creature from the Black Lagoon
Has skin as black as night,
With claws as sharp as razors,
Which tear with all their might.

The creature from the Black Lagoon
Has eyes like scorching irons,
And when he's about to pounce,
He roars like a thousand lions.

The creature from the Black Lagoon
Has teeth as sharp as knives,
And when he digs into his prey,
You can hear their piercing cries.

The creature from the Black Lagoon
Lies on a bed of bones
Awaiting his next challenger
You can hear their dreadful moans.

The creature from the Black Lagoon
Is best left alone,
'Cause if you go to look for him,
You won't be coming home.

Maura Collins (10)
Kippen Primary School, Stirling

If I Had A Kitten

Kittens are so beautiful
With lovely bright eyes
If I had a kitten
It would be a fantastic surprise

Kittens are so funny
They climb up men's ties
If I had a kitten
It would be a lovely surprise

If I had a kitten
It would be a brilliant surprise
I could keep a kitten
It would be the perfect size.

Kirsten Thornton (9)
Kippen Primary School, Stirling

There Was An Old Lady From Spain

There was an old lady from Spain,
In her whole life she'd never seen rain.
Then she came to Scotland . . .
Which wasn't a hot land.
That little old lady from Spain.

There was a man from Peru,
Who couldn't tie his shoe.
One day he tripped over
And got crushed by a bulldozer,
That poor man from Peru.

There was a young girl from Japan,
Who got burnt by a frying pan.
Now she's got a bandage
And can't really manage,
That young girl from Japan.

Michaela Magee (10)
Lady Alice Primary School, Greenock

My Teacher

My teacher is like a summer breeze,
Whistling through the trees.
She is like the summer sun
And a big sugary bun.

My teacher is so cool,
She skateboards to school.
She hates maths and writing
And she's ever so exciting.

My teacher is so rich,
She has her own football pitch.
She has her own swimming pool,
She uses it before school.

At nine o'clock,
She comes in wearing a big pink frock,
One day she came in late,
Smelling of fishing bait.

At lunch she gave
The head teacher a punch,
She ate a strawberry tart,
In the middle of art.

My teacher has blue hair
And likes to be nosy and stare.
Her classroom is so bright
And she doesn't even use a light.

My teacher is the best!

Laura Gillan (10)
Lady Alice Primary School, Greenock

My Little Cousin Scott

My little cousin Scott,
I think he's lost the plot.
He climbed up a tree
And hurt his knee,
My little cousin Scott.

We call him Scotty Wotty
And he's very naughty.
It took him ages to
Get past the potty,
That's Scotty Wotty.

My little cousin Scott,
I think he's lost the plot.
He makes a lot of noise
When playing with his toys.
My little cousin Scott.

Scott likes Scooby-Doo
And Thunderbirds too.
He likes to go to the swimming pool
And he even likes school!

My little cousin Scott,
I think he's lost the plot.
When he shouts you get a sore head,
So I think it's better when he's in bed.

My lovely little cousin Scott.

Lynsey Nicolson (9)
Lady Alice Primary School, Greenock

How I Feel

I feel sad when my dad
Doesn't come down to see me.
He makes me angry and feel really mad,
So I say, 'I hate you Dad!'
Then I feel really bad.

When my nana died, I felt really mad.
I said, 'I wish I'd died.'
Then I felt bad.
I started to cry and felt really sad.

I feel happy when someone says
'Come and dance, sing and prance.
It's a carnival dance!
Come and dance, sing and prance.'
It's a carnival dance!'

My eyes open wide, I hide at night,
Something might give me a fright,
On the stairs in the night.
Squeak, it went!
Creak it went!
Who could it be?
What will they do to me?
Then my sister peeps into the room
And says, 'Can I sleep with you?'

Shareen Lang (11)
Lady Alice Primary School, Greenock

People Say To Me . . .

My dad says to me,
Go away - stop annoying me
Get to your bed!
You're giving me a sore head
Don't do that!
Find the cat!

My mum says to me,
Go make me a cup of tea,
Stop tormenting your brother and sister,
Get me a plaster I've got a blister,
Eat all your tea up,
Christina just shut up!

My teacher says to me,
Put that away,
You have no time to sit and play,
Christina - do your work
And don't give me that horrible smirk.

At the end of the day
You might think I would say
I wish these people would go away!
What I'd really like to say is . . .
Take a hike!
To them of course - not me.

Christina Wilson (11)
Lady Alice Primary School, Greenock

The Calling Of The Waves

The calling of the waves,
How it swishes and it moves.
They're waiting and they're calling
And they're reaching out to you.

The calling of the waves,
They encourage you over,
By washing up charms on the sand.
If you put it to your ear,
It will whisper a secret.

The calling of the waves,
A still and peaceful thought.
You might be feeling blue,
Or you might not.

The calling of the waves,
Using their calm rhythm,
Wishing you under a spell,
I'm taken to a place,
Which I'll never tell.

The calling of the waves,
How it swishes and it moves.
They're waiting and they're calling
And they're reaching out to you.

Selina Chan (11)
Lady Alice Primary School, Greenock

I'm Late

Oh no! I'm late
Someone open the gate!
I'm fast
Oh no, I'm last.
Can someone open the door?
Oh no, I slipped on the floor.
He nearly lost his life
With that big razor-sharp knife!
I mended the bath
I have a funny laugh!
Someone help me please
My friend has the fleas!
He is like a fly
I can't wait to say goodbye.
His name is Joe
And he has a sister called Moe.
So she went back home
And picked up her comb.
Her dad's got a new car
And it's like a star!
Now I'm never late
And I've got a better mate.
Now that's the end of this debate!

Andrew Waddell (11)
Lady Alice Primary School, Greenock

The Family Next Door

The dad is crazy and washes
His car with toilet cleaner.
His room is bright pink
And he drinks his tea
From a baby's bottle.

The mum is also very mad.
She plants weeds instead of flowers
And wears shoes
Three sizes too big for her.

The son is strange.
He plays with Barbie dolls
And goes to ballet dancing.

The daughter is weird.
She takes her budgie
For a walk on a lead.
She stands on her head
When she talks to you.
She also has an Action Man bed cover.

This family is really weird
I think I'll stay out of their way.

Kimberley Stevenson (10)
Lady Alice Primary School, Greenock

Teacher

Teacher! Teacher!
What shall we do with her?
Throw her in the cupboard perhaps?
Miss, I didn't know that you can do raps.

Teacher! Teacher!
What shall we do with her?
Chuck her out the window
And make her sweep the ground,
Then we'll be fine.

Teacher! Teacher!
We're only joking
But how come your head's exploding?

Teacher! Teacher!
What shall we do with her?
Make sure she lets us take over
The day for her.

Teacher! Teacher!
We're only joking
Don't take it personally
We're only children.

Ashleigh Wilson (10)
Lady Alice Primary School, Greenock

All About Feelings

Anger is like a stormy day,
It tastes like a hot spicy curry.
It smells like rotting petrol
And sounds like crashing thunder.
It feels like an old rough stone.

Loneliness feels like nobody cares,
It tastes like rotting Brussels sprouts
And sounds like someone screaming.
It feels like a stoneless ground.

Happiness is like the big bright sun.
It tastes like a bunch of ripe grapes.
It smells like a summery garden
And looks like a calm blue sea.
It sounds like people playing happily.
It feels like hot yellow sand.

Now I would prefer the happiness,
I think you would too.

Samantha Barbour (10)
Lady Alice Primary School, Greenock

My Best Friend

Whenever I'm bored I know what to do
I can always play with my friend Smoo.
She's never dull, she's always fun
Especially when we chase and run.

My dog is very brave and strong
She fights any baddie who comes along.
She's nice and cuddly, she is my best friend
I will love her always, till the very end.

Murray Clark Anderson (8)
Langbank Primary School, Port Glasgow

Seasons In My Garden

In my garden in spring
There is a colourful crocus
Bluebells and buttercups
Lavender and daffodils
And the sound of the frogs croaking.

In my garden in summer
There are apples and plums
Sunflowers and daisies
Ivy and irises
And the sound of the birds singing.

In my garden in autumn
There are wicked weeds
Golden leaves, bonfires burning
Yellow leaves falling off the trees
And the sound of the leaves rustling.

In my garden in winter
There are snowmen and snowballs
Icicles hanging from the railings
Holly and mistletoe hanging from the bars
And the sound of the wind blowing.

Jacqueline Hamilton (9)
Langbank Primary School, Port Glasgow

My Dog Called Islay

She thinks she is a *person!*
She stands on her two black legs
To meet people
And tries to shake hands with you.

She throws a *big orange* ball
In the air
With her front paws.
My dog *Islay!*

Mark Baxter (11)
Langbank Primary School, Port Glasgow

10 Things You Can Do With A Ruler

You can ping it,
You can fling it,
You can throw it on the floor,
You can clean it,
You can use it,
You can throw it out the door,
You can snap it,
You can grab it
And use it to stop the door.

You can ping it,
In the class when the teacher is out,
You can fling it
At the boy who pulled your hair,
You can throw it at the door
And watch it bounce off the floor,
You can ping it on your teeth
And tap it on your desk
And use it to be a pest
And best of all if you need a line,
It will make it straight.

Emma Jones (8)
Langbank Primary School, Port Glasgow

6 Facts About An Alien Maybe

You hardly ever see one
because they live on planet Saturn
with paper and paint
they make a nice pattern.

They will have antennae
and they could be green
and move like a fascinating
mean machine!

Jennifer Mackay (8)
Langbank Primary School, Port Glasgow

The Flu

I feel like a snowman on a hot summer's day,
I can't eat anything or I bring it up in a spray.
It tastes very funny and it hurts my throat
And once I spewed it all over my coat!
I am sick with the flu just lying in bed,
I fear that tomorrow I'll be lying here dead.

I'm here watching films over and over,
I really wish I had that four leaf clover.
It's *the worst* being here without all my friends,
All I want to do is torture toys with pens!
I'll pin their heads up on my wall
And then fling them off a waterfall.
I'll stamp all over their freakish little bodies,
I'll go downstairs and throw them through the lobby!
Being out of school is totally the worst,
I feel so ill I think I might be *cursed!*

Adam Saunders (11)
Langbank Primary School, Port Glasgow

Going To School

I was sitting in the Nissan 350Z
Going very fast round all the bends
When I got to school
I made myself cool.
At playtime I went for a climb
Over the climbing frame.
After school I went to play pool
With my best friends,
The next day I go out to play
Because it's a Saturday.
It is fun . . .
But now I have to . . . run!

Duncan Fletcher (11)
Langbank Primary School, Port Glasgow

Where Is Your Homework?

'Where is your homework?'
'In my bag Sir?'
'Where's your bag?'
'At home Sir.'
'Why is it at home?'
'Well, at least it was at home but it's not now.'
'What are you talking about?'
'My dog took it Sir.'
'And where is your dog?'
'Ran away Sir with my bag right out the door.'
'Well get on with your work.'
'Can't Sir, got no pencil.'
'Why is that?'
'It's in my pencil case.'
'Where is your pencil case?'
'It's with my homework,
In my bag with my dog!'

Iain Gillon (9)
Langbank Primary School, Port Glasgow

School

'You're going to school today
No matter what you say!'
'But Mum! I don't want to go today!'
'Well, you're going to school today,
So go away.'

'Do I have to go to school today.
I don't want food from the dinner lady!'
You're going to school today
So go, go, go away!'

'I'm not going today!'
'Oh yes, you are.'
'But why? Today's Saturday!'

Gillian Hunter (11)
Langbank Primary School, Port Glasgow

My House

Above my house
is the blue, blue sky.
With the white
clouds above.

Beside my house
is a wonderful bush.
A pear tree
with fresh pears on it.

Below my house
is the smelly sewage.
The Hell down below
that will boil you up.

Over my house
is the colourful rainbow
and the birds
tweeting overhead.

Inside my house
is my family.
My sweet loving family.
My noisy, laughing family.
Two dogs
And my cosy furniture.

Beyond my house
is the whole wide world.
My future will be wonderful
no matter what.

Mark Smith   (8)
Langbank Primary School, Port Glasgow

My House

Above my house
is birds talking to each other
clouds white as can be.

Around my house
is the fence
the playhouse
to play mums and dads.

Inside my house
is lots of toys
a widescreen TV
a hat and coat stand.

Beside my house
is the garden gate
and cat and dog
a house for the dog.

Below my house
are rocks and sticks
mud, maybe quicksand.

Over my house
are trees shady as can be,
also there's a rainbow.

Lindsay Birch (8)
Langbank Primary School, Port Glasgow

My House

Above my house
Are some white fluffy clouds
Like white snow.

Beside my house
Is my fruit tree
In winter it is very bare.

Below my house
Is a dirty cold mine
With spiders in it.

Over my house
Is a rainbow with bright colours
Like a magic river.

Inside my house
Is a soft comfy bed
Like a comfy cushion.

Around my house
Is a garden with a long tall wall
Which is the size of a giraffe's neck.

Gemma McKenzie (7)
Langbank Primary School, Port Glasgow

My House

Above my house
is the blue, blue sky,
bright green oak trees towering over it
and the wind that you cannot see.

Beside my house
is a long, sharp path
with a high, high kerb
and a small black gate.

Below my house
is masses of soil
where loads of roots lie
and maybe even dinosaur bones.

Inside my house
is my huge comfy sofa
that I sit on and watch TV.

Around my house are other houses
around the street
with fancy numbers 1 to 10.

Beyond my house is the whole world
where my future dwells with lots of surprises
in store for me.

Ben Saunders (8)
Langbank Primary School, Port Glasgow

Where's Your Homework?

'Where's your homework?'
'Not got it Miss.'
'Why not?'
'It's in the garden Miss!'
'Why?'
'Dog got it Miss.'
'What did the dog do with it?'
'Ran away Miss.'
'Where did it go?'
'Next door Miss.'
'Did he come back?'
'Yes, but he ruined it
and my work was smudged Miss.'
'Why don't you have it?'
'It's wet Miss.'
'Why is it wet?'
'Because of the dog's dribble Miss.'

Fern Fletcher (9)
Langbank Primary School, Port Glasgow

10 Things About Vikings

Viking ships had dragon heads.
I'm sure they didn't have comfy beds.
They have swords, shields and protect helmets too.
Fight and they follow the stars at night.
They have brooches and wear clothes even to bed!
Viking sails were deep blood red.
Odin had a patch and a scratch.
Odin rode a horse and Viking men were called Norse
And Thor was their God to whom they worshipped
They made their own bowls and even made rolls
Vikings used to rule the seas
I wish I could meet a Viking
And ask him more about his life about being a . . . Viking!

Heather McFarlane (7)
Langbank Primary School, Port Glasgow

Late! Late!

'Sweeney! Why are you late?'
'Umm . . . gettin' to watch eighteens, late at night Sir.'
'But you're only nine.'
'I know, I'm lucky Sir.'
'Well, I think you should be sent to detention.'
'It wasn't my fault Sir.'
'Why do you think that?'
'My dad let me watch it Sir.'
'Why are you exhausted Sweeney?'
'I had to chase . . . to chase . . . a Labrador Sir.'
'Why did you have to do that?'
'It ran away with my bag.'
'Can I see your bag please?'
'Yes Sir.'
'Why has it got big holes in it?'
'Cos dogs can't carry bags with their paws.'

Ryan Sweeney (9)
Langbank Primary School, Port Glasgow

Where Is Your Homework?

'Where is your homework?'
'Don't know Miss.'
'Why not?'
'The next-door neighbour's dog got it Miss?'
'How?'
'Don't know Miss.'
'Well has the next-door neighbour's dog still got it?'
'Don't know Miss.'
'Do you know anything about it?'
'Well the dog is called Chloe
and it is a grey-white colour Miss!'
'Not that! Where is the dog?'
'Don't know, it followed me to school then ran off.'
'How did it get it?'
'It didn't tell me Miss!'

Holly Fraser (9)
Langbank Primary School, Port Glasgow

One Day I Was Looking Outside

One day I was looking outside and saw . . .
a beautiful, clear, rippling pond
with lily pads and frogs hopping about
tadpoles and minnows, shiny pink
swimming amongst the pond weed
with the scaly, orange golden fish.

One day I was looking outside and saw . . .
a moist flower bed filled with soil
left by a laughing child and a red plastic spade stuck in,
daffodils, bluebells, pansies all there
as quiet as the wind, as colourful as a rainbow
and as cheerful as the sun
is when he brightens up the day.

One day I was looking outside and saw . . .
green grass all beautifully cut
and the smell of fresh cut grass,
clover and daisies are having pollen sucked out
so we can have sweet golden honey.

Louise Wallwork (9)
Langbank Primary School, Port Glasgow

Without School

I wonder what the world would be like
Without school?
I wonder what people would be like
Without school?
Would we be happy or sad
Without school?
Would there be jobs and houses
Without school?
Would we all be as thick as elephant's skin
Without school?
I don't think I would be happy
Without school.
I don't think anyone would be happy
Without school.
We all do say sometimes
'I really hate school'
But really, deeply in our hearts
We all think,
What would I do
Without school?

Sam Campbell (11)
Langbank Primary School, Port Glasgow

What A Spacecraft Is Like

A spacecraft is round or square.
When it goes by lots of people squint and stare.

A spacecraft whirls about in space.
Two spacecrafts together have a race.

It has funny green buttons
And red ones too.

It even has a sound button
That says moo!

It has flashing blue lights
That go on at night . . .

And if you don't be careful
It will sneak up behind you
And give you a *fright!*

Katie Lapping (8)
Langbank Primary School, Port Glasgow

Gone

As a girl, young or old,
Walked down a path standing bold.
Staring at everyone,
Not knowing what she'd done.

She walked down the path
Where she fell.
We do not know how,
For the trees don't tell.

Then one morning
At the crack of dawn
She stood at a cliff
And suddenly she's gone.

Chiara Bullen (9)
Limerigg Primary School, Falkirk

Animals

An animal can be vicious
and they can be tame as well.
I like all kinds of turtles
that live underneath their shells.

Now rabbits like to run
and dogs like to bark.
Rhinos charge at things
and you'll find cats at the park.

Gorillas are so hairy
they act just like Jim Carrey.
Foxes are so sneaky
and I think snakes are freaky.

I'm running out of animals
to talk about today.
So it's goodbye until next time
so have a nice day.

Johnathan Fisher (11)
Limerigg Primary School, Falkirk

My Best Friend

My friend is bright, bright blue,
She is a nice hot summer
In a secret garden full of flowers
And a clear blue sky.
She is a bright pink jumper
And a lovely cosy bed,
She is a plant programme,
She is a nice wobbly jelly pudding.

Lisa Rushford (10)
Limerigg Primary School, Falkirk

My Best Friend

My best friend is bright blue,
She is summer blue
In a secret garden.
She is a calm, cool sea
And a long fluffy coat.

She is a soft furry pillow
And is Keenan and Kel.
She is an Angel Whip.

She is like a soft little kitten
And a big pink heart.
She is an acrobatic cat
And she is very smart.

Hannah McNeill (10)
Limerigg Primary School, Falkirk

The Wonderful Window

The wonderful window
Is where nobody can see it, only me,
I look at it every day and night.

Butterflies flutter by every day
People lazing under trees doing nothing at all,
Sun streaming like ribbons in the window.

My window is so nice, I want to go outside,
But if I do, the icy snow belts on my face . . .
For summer I have to wait.

Megan Risk (11)
Limerigg Primary School, Falkirk

A Fizzy Drink

A fizzy drink is better than the water out the kitchen sink.
It makes me feel chilled, on a hot summer's day.
I drink it before I go outside and play.
My mum says it will make my teeth rotten,
But I don't believe her because my teeth are as white as cotton!

Nicole McEwan (10)
Limerigg Primary School, Falkirk

Storm At Sea

Sand as smooth as silk
Rock as hard as stone
Sky as clear as crystal
Clouds thick like smoke
Seagulls screeching like a siren
Thunder as loud as a drum
Rain as noisy as footsteps
Waves as tall as buildings
Wind howling like a wolf.

Ross Moffat (11)
Limerigg Primary School, Falkirk

Fizzy Drinks

I like fizzy drinks
The snappy, crackly and poppy kind
The gassy, sizzly and sugary kind
It makes you slurp
It makes you burp
I do like fizzy drinks.

Kim McLuckie (9)
Limerigg Primary School, Falkirk

My Best Friend

My friend is pretty pink
She is like summer on a cloudy day
In a meadow of lambs
And a clear sunset sky.
She is a long flowing skirt,
And a soft furry bed.
She is a holiday programme
And a sticky toffee pudding.

Demi Johnstone (10)
Limerigg Primary School, Falkirk

Summer Days

The hot sun blazing,
Faces sweating, feeling lazy.
In the garden Granny's knitting,
Kids playing, drinking ice-cold cocktails,
People sitting, having fun,
Out on day trips everyone,
But when the days come to an end,
We all wish it was summer again.
Summer days are so nice!

Carys Williams (10)
Limerigg Primary School, Falkirk

The Sun

I like the sun
The round, smooth and warm kind
I like the sun because it's warm
I do like the sun.

Johnathan Beattie (9)
Limerigg Primary School, Falkirk

Rain

I love rain
The sploshy, splashy, puddly kind
I love splashing in the puddles
And singing in the rain
I do love the rain.

Erin Risk (9)
Limerigg Primary School, Falkirk

Facing The Bullies

They called me Giant with the face of a shoe.
Oh well, I'm ten times the size of you.
They called me Kangaroo with a lot of fear.
I said, 'That's nowhere near.'
They called me a big-headed freak.
I said, 'At least I'm not weak.'
They called me a weirdo with the clothes of a tramp.
At least inside, I know I'm a champ.

They got bored and left me alone.
Now I live in a bully-free zone.

Marc Stables (10)
Longstone Primary School, Edinburgh

From My Window

From my window I see trees
Swaying at the bottom of my garden to get my attention.
And I can also see hills, covered in snow.
They look so cold I shiver.
There goes a fox in its lovely fur coat,
He's not shivering like me.
From my window I see birds in the sky,
Flying away as the darkness falls.

Lauren Anderson (8)
Longstone Primary School, Edinburgh

Inside A Boy's Head

Inside a boy's head
He's playing football
He's wearing the green shirt
His favourite team,
Hibernian
And he's the star.

Inside a boy's head
Bertie Vogts is watching,
The boy has talent
Could he soon be playing for his country?
He's a wizard with that ball
The fans, he thrills them all.

Mark Hanlon (9)
Longstone Primary School, Edinburgh

July

July is a sunny month
The sun is shining up in the sky
Bright green grass to play on
Beaches on holiday
Friends to make
Play in the sea
Loads of excitement
Party all day
Go out to dinner with my family
Fun, fun, fun all day long
Time to go back to bed and start *again!*

Leigh McMahon (8)
Longstone Primary School, Edinburgh

The Bully

The bully loomed above me
With a smirk upon her face
My hands shook frantically
I tried to hide my thoughts of fear
The bully grabbed my arm and squeezed hard
My eyes were widening
Minute by minute
She kicked my leg and grinned
'Stop,' I shouted loudly
Causing an echo through the school
I tried to free myself
I squirmed and squealed
'Stop,' I screamed again and gritted my teeth
The bully cackled aloud
And eventually stomped off
I smiled
I'd done it all myself.

Lauren Notman (10)
Longstone Primary School, Edinburgh

Under The Sea

Angelfish swimming
The lights are dimming
Shellfish clattering
Starfish chattering
Swordfish cutting
Fishermen hurting
Divers jumping
Fishes bumping
Teenage fish racing
Baby fish missing
Sea plants waving
Mother fish caring
Sharks biting
Bigger fish fighting.

Zoe McRae (9)
Longstone Primary School, Edinburgh

Football

Football, football, football, football
I just love playing football
The ball is passed
The ball is shot
It gets put out and it goes to pot.

Players running up and down
Players running all around
Players pushing
Players tackling
Players hurt down on the ground.

Players sweating from the game
Players shouting for the ball
Five minutes left - can that be all?
The fans are crowded in a shoal
Then finally, I scored the goal!

Kenny O'Brien (10)
Longstone Primary School, Edinburgh

My Parrot Mac

My parrot is an African grey
He loves to sing and he loves to play
He's very fussy with his food
And doesn't say things that are rude
His tail is shiny, crimson red
He loves to perch on my mum's head
He is learning how to talk
But he prefers to bite and squawk
He gets a biscuit from my mum
And chews at every single crumb
He whistles till you call his name
His name is Mac and he's very tame.

Ben Brigg (10)
Longstone Primary School, Edinburgh

The Hurricane

Hurricane, hurricane
Starts from a storm
Hurricane, hurricane
On and on
Hurricane, hurricane
Touch the ground
Hurricane, hurricane
Swirling round
Hurricane, hurricane
At 160 kilometres per hour
Hurricane, hurricane
Hour by hour
Hurricane, hurricane
Getting high
Hurricane, hurricane
Passing by
Hurricane, hurricane
Sweeping up
Hurricane, hurricane
Making people fed up
Hurricane, hurricane
Calming down
Hurricane, hurricane
Slowing down
Hurricane, hurricane
Watching eye
Hurricane, hurricane
You will die
Hurricane, hurricane.

Lisa-Marie Kennedy (11)
Longstone Primary School, Edinburgh

Is It Real?

Power lines stretch across the land
visiting houses and chatting to a million people a day.

Houses stare at the clouds slipping by,
never moving from their spot.

Cars cruise down the street
gobbling up people every time they stop.

Wheelie bins swallow bags of smelly rubbish
then spit them out in the morning.

The grass cutter munches
on mounds of hairy grass.

Grit boxes spray salt
persuading the ice to disappear.

John Allan (11)
Longstone Primary School, Edinburgh

31st Of October

Hallowe'en is coming, the night is getting dark.
Beware of witches, ghosts and goblins as you cross the park.
Some are black, some are white, others they are green.
You'll get a fright if they are seen rolling across the village green.
Broomsticks, cats and mice, will have you thinking twice,
Before you venture out on a haunted Hallowe'en night.
Make sure it's your mother and not a witch when you return home
Or else you may wish that you were home alone.

Rebecca Scott (10)
Longstone Primary School, Edinburgh

The Hurricane

Hurricane, hurricane swirling round
Hurricane, hurricane always to be found
Crushing up houses, sweeping paths
Here it comes - run away fast!

Hurricane, hurricane higher and higher
Hurricane, hurricane will you please retire
Faster and faster this hurricane goes
Where will it go next? Nobody knows.

Eating up fences, chopping down trees
The hurricane stops, everyone's free
Hurricane, hurricane just a little wind
The bad stuff has gone and the trash is binned.

Laura Small (11)
Longstone Primary School, Edinburgh

July

July is my favourite time of the year.
Trees are calling on you to come out to play.
The blue sky just seems so warm.
Grass is green and orange,
The crops are growing brightly,
Flowers lift their faces to the bright glow of the sun.
Happy children having fun,
Parents relaxing in the sun.

July, yes, it's my favourite time of the year!

Robbie Jack (9)
Longstone Primary School, Edinburgh

Free From Bullies

Bully free and worry free
Really good, they don't touch me
Every night I get to sleep
Every morning I don't weep
The good thing is when I go to school
I never, ever get called a fool
Like big-head, fatty
Or mashed patatie
If anyone tries to give me a blow
I stand up to them and just say, 'Ho!'

Natalie Prosser (10)
Longstone Primary School, Edinburgh

Millie

I have a dog called Millie
Who likes to play all day
Sometimes she is silly
And barks at those who stray
The garden is her favourite place
Where she can watch us play
She buries her bone at a very quick pace
Then off she goes to play.

David Wright (10)
Longstone Primary School, Edinburgh

The Hurricane

The hurricane swirling at 160 miles an hour
Violent, angry, furious,
Like a whirlpool raging in the ocean
Like an angry bulldog barging through the city
It makes me feel like a tiny bug on the ground
Like a piece of litter blown away in the autumn wind.
The hurricane makes me realise how precious life is.

Elliot Lindsay (11)
Longstone Primary School, Edinburgh

The Monster

There's a monster in my bedroom, Mum
I'll tell you what it's like.
Its head is like a big sack of potatoes.
Its body like a huge maggot squirming in an owl's pellet.
Its claws are like a sloth climbing up a tree.
Its teeth like a vampire going to drink blood.
I know you don't believe me, Mum
But hurry up, it's getting closer,
It's . . . 'Argh!'

Emma Kelly (11)
Longstone Primary School, Edinburgh

An Ode To A Cheesecake

Fit a fine tangy smell ye are
Sitting on a plate!
Yir like a roond circle
Just waiting to be ate!

White, reed and yella tee
It's awfa fine sicht to see
Wae a smooth top an'
A crumbly bottom - it's awfa scrumptious tae me!

Gyaad sakes! Heinz beans!
It's enough tae mak ye spew
It'll pooshen me an' even - you!
It's vile, mingin, stinking - phew!
Unlike mi cheesecake
Fit a bonny moothfoo!

There's nothing like a moo-watterin' cheesecake
Tae brichten up ma day!

George Imlach (11)
Macduff Primary School, Macduff

An Ode Tae Ma Dad's Labster

Biled tae a bonnie reed,
Seen tae us ye'll mak a fine feed
From the tip o'yer tail tae the tap o yer heid.
Inside y'er a lovely fite,
On a plate yer a braw sight,
Y'er cut inta squares as sma as a bead,
After you've been caught frae the seaweed.

Because o'yer looks some folk are put off
But in yer moo it's nice an' saft,
Nae pork frae a pig or beef frae a calf,
Tae keep it fresh ma dad keeps it live in the bath!

Steamy, green an' fluffy aboot,
It can mak the bravest man shoot,
A hope a never see the day,
I have to eat a stick o' broccoli,
They say it's healthy an' gweed for ye,
But I'd rather hae lobster for ma tae!

Aye! The lobster's fine fer a treat,
There's nuthin' better than labster meat,
That's fit I think, but maybe you dinna,
But if I got tae choose it would be lobster -
Fer dinner!

James Milne (11)
Macduff Primary School, Macduff

An Ode To Ma Mam's Mince Pie

Ma fine mince pie!
Ma mam made ye awfa gweed,
Yer sittin' in yer plate
Knowing yer fate!
Pastry, mince and carrots!

Ye fill ma belly,
Fin I hae one too mony!
It's a glorious sicht,
And I micht, just micht
Tak' one mare bite,
O ma mam's mince pie!

I hate a thon haggis,
For I hate the taste!
If I tak a bite,
It'll pooshen me,
It's mingin, stinkin an' vile!

Haggis is no match for ma mam's mince pie
It's weet inside an' ootside it's dry,
It melts in yer moo,
And comes fae a coo!
It smells awfa fine,
It's ma mam's - good aul', fine mince pie!

John Percival (11)
Macduff Primary School, Macduff

An Ode To Ma Mam's Hame-Made Bolognese

O ma mam's hame-made Bolognese the best.
The Hale family thinks it's awfa braw.
The spaghetti is like wiggly worms
But the taste is jist so fine.
I'd ate and ate the nivver stop
The sauce is so reed and gweed!
The Bolognese looks sae bonny, sitten in its plate,
Oh the day I'd really hate haein' to ate
Thon broccoli and cauliflower
Them English fowlk would sit an laugh
At ma mam's Bolognese!
Ma mam an dad would mak me eat a' this rotten gulsh.
These veggies are sae manky
I'd rather ate a hunky!
Ma mam's bolognese is the best, better than a' thae rest.

Heidi Watt (11)
Macduff Primary School, Macduff

An Ode Ta A Fry-Up

Grizzly, broon, pink an' reed
Comes fae animals that are deed.
Grizzly bacon, pink an' crispy
Sausages - soggy an' fine!
Nice eggs wae a yoke
An' that's nae joke!
I would eat you as fast as I can
Fan I see ye in the frying pan!

I hate that reekin' macaroni an' cheese
Don't make me eat it - I ask you - please!
It could couk a dog, and even a frog!
Fooshtie, hummin' fish is nae match for a fry-up!
You are gweed on a Sunday morning fin I've just woken up
It's braw tae see ye sittin' sa bonnie on a plate
I'm nae needin' onie o' at foreign muck that I hate!

Scott Gillies
Macduff Primary School, Macduff

An Ode To My Granny's Cullen Skink

Oh mi granny's cullen skink
Fit an awfa sicht,
It's a awfa fine smooth feeling inside yer moo,
After you feel like a stuffed coo,
O but I must
Nae forget the veg and the fish,
Mixed through and through,
Only I wish I could hae it richt noo!

O it's such a nice smell,
You could smell it fae a mile awa,
It's so fine and bricht,
The colours are yalla and white
O it's just richt!

O bit thon brocolli,
It's so vile and stinking,
An it tastes so mingin,
I just cana be buthert wae it,
It's enough to make you sick and spew,
O I don't want to put it in ma moo,
Neither would you!

I'm glad to hae a granny,
That makes me lovely cullen skink,
She makes it so fine and gweed,
O the thought of the smell goes through ma heed,
O I love it wae a bit o breed,
I wish I could put it in ma moo,
Richt noo!

Sarah Cowie (11)
Macduff Primary School, Macduff

An Ode To Ma Mam's Baked Tatties And Prans

O ma mam's baked tatties are awfa gweed,
The broon tyooch, crispy skin covered in sat,
Fin the butter melts the smell is awfa fine,
An' it melts in ma moo.

The pinky colour o' the prans fae Tesco,
Ya hiv an awfa fine taste,
An' together sittin', ya ken fine fits gan to happen to ya,
An' ya dinna want to go, do ya?
But in ma moo is far ya should be!

At trifle looks fooshtie - it's enough ti mak ya spew,
An' at Brussel sproots - they winna be whining 'cause they wina get
eaten if they're on my plate,
Oh! 'at cooked carrots! They're manky, rotten things,
They're much better raw,
If I hid tae choose I wid choose me mam's baked tatties an' prans,
I widnae ate any o' at foreign muck! Y'er an awfa bonnie sight,
An' ya go roon me heart,
Ye'r so gweed I want ya noo,
Ya mak ma moo fairly watter!

Nicola Hadden (11)
Macduff Primary School, Macduff

An Ode To Bacon And Sausages

At's an awfa bonnie looking sausage ma mam made tae me
She ayewis maks it perfect never makes it raw
Of course fits a sausage waeoot a bit o'bacon
Seems like a day she's been makin'!

Jist looking at yi
It's awfa broon
It'll be gone very soon!
It's mair an' fine so it wid be kind
If ye could mak anither een for a growin' loon!

It's heaps better'an at vile carrots and beans
Tae ate a 'em - I'm nae awfa keen
If I wiz forced tae try I 'em-
I wid hae neen!
Makin' ma ate at is awfa mean
'Ats I worst thing I've ivver seen!
An i's the worst thing I've iver deen!

Aye! I'll stick to ma sausages and bacon
It's at vile beans I'm hatin
It's I best thing I've ivver eaten
It's sausages and bacon that canna be beaten!

Ewan Forbes (11)
Macduff Primary School, Macduff

An Ode Ti Baxters Tomata Soup!

Sittin' ere a' in reed
Ye'r looking afa gweed!
In i bowl I can say ye'r i best thing that is ivver made,
A' reed in i bowl wae a little touch o' herbs
Oh if you tried 'at gweed 'reed stuff
Ye couldna hae nithing better!

O' at mushy tattie Heinz baked beans,
They're a'reed an' nae sae gweed,
Oh . . . if you tried 'at fooshtie dirt I'm sure ye'd couk!

But if you tried at tomata soup ye'd hae it a'i time,
So ging awa an' ask yer mam, if she wid pit on a tin,
An' if ye do - which I think ye will
Ye'd hae it for every denner!

Ryan West (11)
Macduff Primary School, Macduff

In Sixty Years' Time

In sixty years' time when I'm seventy-one
I'll remember the days when I sung
I did not like it one bit
And my mum gave a little hit.

In sixty-one years' time when I'm seventy-two
I'll remember the days when I met you
You said to me will you play with me
I said yes and do you want some candy?

In sixty-two years' time when I'm seventy-three
I'll remember the days when I was three
I fell down stairs in my baby walker
I had a broken arm and a little cracker.

Alexander Robertson (10)
Nethermains Primary School, Denny

In Sixty Years' Time

In sixty years' time
When I am seventy-one
I will remember the time
When I fell on my bum

In sixty years' time
When I am seventy-one
I will remember the time
When I broke my thumb.

In sixty years' time
When I am seventy-one
I will remember the time
When I lost Mum.

In sixty years' time
When I am seventy-one
I will remember the time
When I always had fun.

In sixty years' time
When I am seventy-one
I will remember the time
When I wrote this poem.

Steven Jackson
Nethermains Primary School, Denny

My Baby Brother

When I was holding my baby brother I felt excited.
He was small and warm, so I never let go.
He smiled at me, I started to laugh.
I gave him back to my mum and he started to cry
And then I wished he was grown up.

Ben McVickers (11)
Nethermains Primary School, Denny

My Nephew

My nephew is as sweet as honey.
His hair is like the shiny bright sun.
His eyes are like the blue wintry sky.
His face is like a very soft cloth.
When he walks he is as big as a mirror.
When he sits he is like a tiny teddy.
When he laughs he is like a little joker.
When he sleeps he is like a tiny teddy in bed.
The best thing about my nephew
Is he is as cute as anything you can find.

Callum Mincher (9)
Nethermains Primary School, Denny

Holding The Baby

Holding my sister,
They said I could hold her
In the hospital to get a photograph.
Then they told me
This will be a laugh.

They told me to snuggle her
Up tight so she doesn't fall
And get a fright.

Now she is grown up
And I can't hold her because
She is not a baby any longer.

Andrew Bain (11)
Nethermains Primary School, Denny

My Dad

My dad is as bright as a shining star.
His hair is like chocolate melting in a pot.
His eyes are like marbles glowing in the dark.
His face is like a ball when it is brand new.
When he walks he is like a tortoise walking on the path.
When he sits he is like a snake curled on a tree.
When he laughs he is like a pig when it is eaten.
When he sleeps he is like a lion under a tree.
The best thing about my dad is he will always be there for me.

David Gordon (11)
Nethermains Primary School, Denny

Winter's Poem

Looked out the window on a winter's day,
Saw some snow and went out to play.
It got a little bit colder in the afternoon,
It started to rain, the snow will go soon.

Everybody has walked in the snow, crush, crush,
Now it's turning into slush.
It's so cold you have to wear hat and mits
And the council will be coming round with grit.

Finally the snow has gone,
You can see the garden lawn.
Soon spring will be here
And the rain will disappear.

Josh Dishington (11)
Pitreavie Primary School, Dunfermline

Chocolate

C hildren love chocolate
H ungry for chocolate
O h! how lovely it is
C hocolate, chocolate, chocolate
O h! I love it
L ovely is the word for chocolate
A fabulous treat
T asty chocolate
E xcellent taste.

Kirsten Hamilton (9)
Ralston Primary School, Paisley

To A Yorkie

Y ummy
O nly eat it on Friday
R eally milky
K ids love it
I t's not for girls only tomboys
E asy to get addicted.

B est chocolate in the world
A re you brave enough to try it?
R elaxing!

Paula Gahagan (9)
Ralston Primary School, Paisley

My Favourite Food - Cakes

C reamy, strawberry too
A lovely treat
K it-Kat flavour
E at it all up
S ick, you might be.

Calum McLean (9)
Ralston Primary School, Paisley

My Pet Dog

M y pet dog's fluffy and cuddly
Y ellow coloured hair and brown eyes

P urple collar and brown feet
E ven if he is smelly he is still a dog
T onight we are going to the park to play on the hills

D ogs are everyone's best friend
O ften they go outside and get dirty
G ood behaved dog and I love him.

Gillian Breslin (9)
Ralston Primary School, Paisley

To A Steak Pie

S imply the best
T remendously tasty
E nriching flavour
A t the restaurant I order steak pie,
K icking flavour.

P retty good
I ncredibly delicious
E nough after a few courses.

Alasdair Forrest (9)
Ralston Primary School, Paisley

My Friend

This is my friend in the rain
I like her because she isn't a pain
And she has got the same name
Now I play with her every day
And I never have to say I don't want to play
She likes playing football
But she isn't tall or too small.

Amy Watters (9)
Ralston Primary School, Paisley

Tilly My Pet Dog

T illy is my pet dog
I really like her because she is cute
L ovely growing dog
L ove having her
Y ou would like her too

M y dog is very loud
Y ap! Yap! Yap!

P et dogs are great
E ven when they bark
T oday Tilly kept me busy

D ogs play with balls
O scar is my other dog
G et a dog soon!

Leigh Baxter (9)
Ralston Primary School, Paisley

Chocolate

C ocoa beans give it flavour.
H eavenly taste.
O range chocolate is really sweet.
C hocolate I love it very much.
O h! the taste is so delicious.
L ots of it makes you sick.
A lot of people do eat it.
T asty and scrumptious.
E ating it makes me happy.

Blair Dalgleish (9)
Ralston Primary School, Paisley

Yum-Yum In My Tum

C urry, luscious, lovely.
H onourable to like.
I love curry
C hecking it out, it's not too spicy for me
K ing of all foods
E ating it on Saturday is when I have mine
N othing can compare

T aking out of the packet, spilling it on my plate
I t makes me happy to see it on my plate
K icking off a Saturday night
K ashmiri or Goan
A food to behold

C ome on let's go get it
H ot and ready to eat
A s good as playing in seven inch snow
S uper spices from India
N icest of all
A curry is fantastic
I 'll have some rice with that please!

Ross Gibson (9)
Ralston Primary School, Paisley

Chocolate

C ocoa beans make it very nice
H eavenly, tasty I think
O range chocolate is fabulous
C hocolate, I like it
O rdinary chocolate is soft and sweet
L ots of it makes you sick
A lot of people like chocolate
T asty and scrumptious
E ating it makes me feel fabulous.

Laura Russell (9)
Ralston Primary School, Paisley

Humpty Dumpty

Humpty Dumpty sat on the beach
Humpty Dumpty ate a great peach
All the king's horses and all the king's men
Couldn't peel Humpty's peach ever again.
I don't think it was very fair Humpty floated in the air.
Then he ate a big pear, then he came down from the air.
His sugar paper filled with shame
Made him want to play a game.

Emma Ross (9)
Ralston Primary School, Paisley

Chocolate

C hewy, chunky chocolate
H eavenly, tastes just the same
O ut in shops everywhere
C overed in chocolate, yum-yum!
O ne taste and you will love it
L ovely, lumpy chocolate
A ll children love it
T rying hard to stop eating it
E veryone likes chocolate, yeah, yeah, yeah!

Allyson Craig (9)
Ralston Primary School, Paisley

Seasons

W inter is a bad season
I don't like the rain very much
N o one plays outside in the rain
T hen I love it when it snows at Christmas
E very so often I play with friends
R ain is not very nice for animals.

Kenneth Wright (9)
Ralston Primary School, Paisley

My Favourite Thing

F ootball is a good sport
O n the pitch Lovenkrands plays on the left wing
O liver Kahn is the best goalie in the world
T he best Brazilian player is Ronaldo of Real Madrid
B arcelona's best player is Ronaldinho
A rteta is my favourite Rangers' player
L jungberg is a good Arsenal player
L aurent Robert of Newcastle is great with his shots.

Connor McNair (9)
Ralston Primary School, Paisley

Summer

S ummer is the best time of year
U p and down the sun goes
M arvellous time I have in the heat
M ake a sandcastle at the beach
E ven my birthday is in that month
R unning around with my friends.

Lauren Park (9)
Ralston Primary School, Paisley

Kitten Poem

K itty cat, kitty cat
I love insy winsy kitty cats
T iny, sweet kitty cats
T hey're cute and kind, running around
E xtraordinary creatures
N ice, cuddly kitty cat.

Nicole Barnes (9)
Ralston Primary School, Paisley

Favourite Things

F ootball games rule
A rt kits are cool
V ideos are great
O ur toys are special
U nder the doll's house are spiders
R ubbish toys are cheap
I gnore Barbies
'T rue Crime', 'Streets of LA' are like 'Grand Theft Auto'
'E nter The Matrix' is really fandabbiedosy

T oys rule the world
H e who hates toys is daft
I n the house is like toy town
N o toys for over 18's
G nomes ain't cool
S uperhero toys are No 1.

Stuart MacLean (9)
Ralston Primary School, Paisley

Perfect Pussy

P ussy cats love you
E xcited and purring around your legs
R ats and mice they catch
F riends of mine they are
E xcited and interested in what you do
C ats are so cute
T hey like you to play with them.

P urrfect they are!
U nder a tree in the shade they sit
S mokey's black and very sweet
S mudge is black and white, very cute
Y ou just can't help loving cats!

Jennifer Hale (9)
Ralston Primary School, Paisley

A Nougat

A nougat is nutritious.
I could eat them all day.
It is sweet and delightful.
When I eat it I am in Heaven.
It is chewy, smooth, soft and creamy.
It smells nice, it makes me hungry.
The flavour is ordinary.
It makes my mouth water.
It is glorious and it is pleasant.
It is nutty and very tasteful.
It is even nicer than orange chocolate.

Hannah Douglas (9)
Ralston Primary School, Paisley

Emma

E mma is my best friend
M e and Emma make up dances to songs
M e and Emma always have each other
A imee is one of Emma's friends too.

Devon McGuiness
Ralston Primary School, Paisley

Humpty Dumpty

Humpty Dumpty had lovely feet
Humpty Dumpty liked his feet
Humpty Dumpty smelled his feet
Humpty Dumpty fell asleep.

Natasha Robinson (9)
Ralston Primary School, Paisley

Glorious Food

C hildren love it
H eaven is just as nice
O ur favourite food
C hildren love it lots
O ld ladies even like it
L ots of people eat it daily
A lways tastes good
T op chocolate bar
E asily eaten.

B ut lots of shops don't do Team
A re you a chocolate fan?
R eally it's my favourite food.

Chelsea Kelly (9)
Ralston Primary School, Paisley

Toffo My Cat

T offo was a friendly cat
O h how we laughed and played
F or hours we would tumble
F or hours we would rumble
O ur memories will not fade.

Sarah Watters (9)
Ralston Primary School, Paisley

My Dogs

I have two dogs called Molly and Maisy,
Sometimes they are a little lazy.
Most of the time they play around,
Enjoying knocking me to the ground!
At other times they like to fight,
Jumping about from left to right -
But most of all every day
They like me home to start to play.

Fraser Barnes (11)
Rashielea Primary School, Erskine

My Hard Life

Here I am
Sitting on a thin, small stool
Opening and shutting doors
I cry

I take a sip of water
And a bit of stale bread
I struggle to stay awake
I work from dawn to dusk

My master comes
I'm asleep
He whips me
I try not to cry

My shift is over
I go out
I give a smile
And then drift away.

Corinne Hepburn (9)
St Andrew's Primary School, Falkirk

Satan's Den

I walk in the cave,
I lean against the jagged wall,
I bleed and cry.

The agony and pain,
The anger,
The hunger and thirst.

The hell hole,
I dare not fall asleep,
The pain makes me cry in horror,
I know my shift is over,
I walk with a small smile, but it fades.
        God help me.

Claire Moore (9)
St Andrew's Primary School, Falkirk

I Have A Dream

(Based on 'I Have A Dream' speech by M L King)

I have a dream
No one gets hurt.
I have a dream
That there are no jails.
I have a dream
That there is no such thing as hunger.
I have a dream
No one dies of slavery.
I have a dream
There are no weapons.
I have a dream
No one's bullied because of their colour.
I have a dream
Everyone gets on with each other.

Danielle Kelly (9)
St Andrew's Primary School, Falkirk

I Have A Dream

(Based on 'I Have A Dream' speech by M L King)

I have a dream of no war or terrorism.
Of peace and happiness,
And no starvation or thirst.
Of good education for children,
And they can play without fear.

I have a dream of no racism,
Or violence.
For all the black skinned
To be treated as well as the white,
And the binds of slaves will break.

I have a dream of peace,
But will it come true?
Only God knows.

Ryan Irwin (9)
St Andrew's Primary School, Falkirk

I Have A Dream

(Based on 'I Have A Dream' speech by M L King)

I have a dream
that no one is hurt.
I have a dream
people are safe.
I have a dream
that no one knows what hunger is.
I have a dream
that there are no jails because no one is bad.
I have a dream
there is no crime in the world.
I have a dream
that black and white live in peace.

I have lots of dreams
but these are
the best ones of all!

Joanne Conlin (9)
St Andrew's Primary School, Falkirk

Up In The Darkness

Up in the darkness every day
Blistered elbows and blistered knees
My master shouting at me, 'Hurry up!'
I am tired and hungry
The dust is getting into my lungs
I cough.

Up in the thin, black, narrow chimney
I am cold
I cry
Back again tomorrow
I am terrified
Long hours tomorrow.

Liana Cardillo (9)
St Andrew's Primary School, Falkirk

I Have A Dream

(Based on 'I Have A Dream' speech by M L King)

I have a dream
That no one owns humans.
I have a dream
That war has no beginning.
I have a dream
That humans' love will never end.
I have a dream
That wounds from fights will start to mend.
I have a dream
And want it to stay.
I have a dream
That no one knows the word racism.
I have a dream
Of a world full of love.
I have a dream
That humans act the way they should.
How can this be true?
Stand together and bring it to life
Let's stop the fights
And start with peace.

Sean Graves (9)
St Andrew's Primary School, Falkirk

The Eagle

There he stands on his crooked castle,
Waiting to strike his final blow.
His eyes scan the ground like prison searchlights,
Then he swoops like lightning and doesn't blink an eye.
He digs his talons into his enemy.
Hear the blood-curdling echoes of his prey
Then he takes it back to his lair
To devour his meal.

Ross Flaherty (9)
St Andrew's Primary School, Falkirk

Talking To People Who Live In The Dark

Red is the colour of a hot, blazing fire or the taste of sweet
tomato soup,
Green is the taste of a freshly picked apple and the touch of
the mushy seaweed at the beach.
Gold is the colour of a noisy brass band in the hot sun.
Black is the feeling of something scary inside and the sad feeling
of someone passing away.
Orange is the feeling of a family day out or happiness on a birthday.
Blue is the smell of a blueberry pie and lying on your back outside
on a beautiful day.
White is the feel of snowflakes on your hand and the sound
of the crashing waves.
Silver is the sound of a fairy's tinkling bell and the sound of plates
crashing together.
Pink is the colour of ballerinas dancing.

Rebecca Scullion (9)
St Andrew's Primary School, Falkirk

I Have A Dream

(Based on 'I Have A Dream' speech by M L King)

I have a dream that I will share,
All human beings are happy and fair.
There will be sun but never showers,
People will turn back time and save the Twin Towers.

There aren't any clinics because no one is ill,
There aren't any jails because no one will kill.
Women and children and men all have rights,
Everyone has a house to sleep in at night.

Poverty, slavery and war have all stopped,
Guns and knives and daggers were dropped.
No adults or parents are cruel,
Children nationwide all go to good schools.

Ruth McElroy (9)
St Andrew's Primary School, Falkirk

A Spider's Web

A bewitching sight, silently spinning in a hidden place.

S parkling, sticky, silky trap.
P athetic, blissfully ignorant fly shoots through the air.
I ncredible speed the spider uses to get his prey . . .
the hunter is rewarded.
D ead lies the fly, the spider retreats to his deadly abode.
E erie silence fills the hunter's lair . . .
R uthless predator, murdering scum . . .
S himmering creation, mended by its inhabitants.

W retched beast, slaughtering the innocent.
E legant web, merciless murderer, mysterious secrets lurk within . . .
B ouncing gently in the wind . . . an insect's worst nightmare.

Lorna Stallard (11)
St Andrew's Primary School, Falkirk

Fireworks

Fiery fireworks twinkling in the coal-black sky
Impressing the children, ever so high
Catherine wheels spinning round and round
Until they fall to the ground.

Roman candles showering so bright
Giving all the children a wonderful sight
Red, blue, yellow and green
They are the colours that you have seen.

Zooming rockets in the sky
Exploding in a wink of an eye
Screamers bursting ever so high
Into the cold, black evening sky.

Luana-Hai Taljaard (9)
St Andrew's Primary School, Falkirk

The Box Of Dreams

(Based on by 'Magic Box' by Kit Wright)

In my box of magic dreams there will be . . .
A glorious sunset,
The softness of a gossamer wing,
The contentment of a purring cat,
And the beauty of a ballet pose.

In my box of dreams there will be . . .
The warmth of the sun,
The happiness of my family,
And the exhilaration of a racing car
Speeding away in the distance.

In my box of magic dreams there will be . . .
Only laughter and happiness,
No sadness or unhappiness,
Just dreams of happiness.

In my magic box
That is what there is!

Shauna Chalmers (10)
St Andrew's Primary School, Falkirk

Fireworks

Humming fireworks in the coal black sky
Shooting up ever so high
Children watching everywhere
Amazed with all the atmosphere.

Catherine wheels spinning sweetly
Amazing how they twirl so neatly
Rockets zooming in the sky
Wonderful colours shooting by.

Roman candles spinning round
Rushing down to the ground
What a beautiful sight to see
Sharing their delight with you and me.

Sarah Dawson (9)
St Andrew's Primary School, Falkirk

The Magic Box

(Based on 'Magic Box' by Kit Wright)

In my box I will put . . .
The freshness of spring,
The diamond from a ring,
And the voice of a singing king.

In my box I will put . . .
The yummy French food oh la la!
The horrible slithery snakes,
And little cute pink and blue bunnies.

My box will be fashioned with
Pink and purple snow,
With stars and Mars bars all in a row,
With pretty pink bows.
My box will also have babies smiling with a glow.

My box is full of lots of treats,
Some nice, some horrible, some indescribable.
My box is full of presents for me,
I hope some will be sweets and tea.

Charlotte-Ann Stoddart (10)
St Andrew's Primary School, Falkirk

Talking To People Who Live In The Dark

Blue is the touch of a very cold piece of ice straight from the freezer.
Black is the scary feeling of a bad dream in total darkness
And the sad, lonely feeling of your friend dying and leaving.
Red is like being beside a very relaxing fire on a fluffy rug.
Gold is a happy feeling of your birthday and opening your presents.

Orange is a really good day at the beach in the hot sun when
You are lying on the warm sand with the sun beating down on you.
Green is the smell of the freshly cut grass and the smell of fresh air.
Silver is the touch of a really cold iceberg and the frozen lake in winter.

Dylan Baty (9)
St Andrew's Primary School, Falkirk

Young Writers - Once Upon A Rhyme Scotland

A Spider's Web

A raindrop hanging from a net of silk.

S pilling over the web and gently falling to the ground.
P erfect web blowing in the wind.
I n the centre lies a small spider.
D eadly, waiting for its prey.
E ndless concentration.
R esting on the small web.
S omething's caught - an insect!

W ondering, trapped in the web it silently screams.
E ight legs scurrying across the web, it pounces, stabs
    the small creature, injects it with its poison.
B eating heart! Open eyes! Paralysed! Dead!

Stephanie Carrier (11)
St Andrew's Primary School, Falkirk

Gran Poem

My gran is as lovely as a bush of beautiful roses.
Her hair is like the baby brown chestnut.
Her eyes are like beautiful blue icebergs.
Her face is like the beautiful, happy sun rising.
When she walks she is like a steam train pushing and pushing.
When she sits she is like a stuffed little teddy.
When she laughs she is like a singing fairy.
When she sleeps she is like a mouse.
The best things about my gran are she is loving, caring
and most of all she makes me laugh!
I love her.

Nicholas Wylie (9)
St Andrew's Primary School, Falkirk

Fireworks

Rockets zooming into the coal-black sky
Exploding and booming away up high
Purple, blue, green and white
A rainbow of colours
A beautiful sight.

Catherine wheels spin round and round
So fast, such fun
And then fall to the ground.

Roman candles like the waterfall
So beautiful and bright
Glistening like a golden trophy
They're beautiful at night.

Rosie Ferrier (9)
St Andrew's Primary School, Falkirk

The Parade

The joyful parade is on its way,
On a lovely sunny day.
I listen to the cheerful song,
They don't even get a note wrong.

Then the men's voices are singing,
Then the jingling bells are ringing.
The crowd are all tapping their feet,
To this cheerful, joyful beat.

The voices are now all faint,
And where is the banging beat?
The parade is now fading away,
I hope they will come another day.

Rachel Doherty (10)
St Andrew's Primary School, Falkirk

Magic Box

(Based on 'Magic Box' by Kit Wright)

I will put into my box . . .
The first word of a baby
The magnificent food of a chef
A sculpture of a wood carver.

I will put into my box . . .
The joy of poetry
The kids working at school
An English man learning Scottish.

I will put into my box . . .
The laughter of a joke
The first miracle of Jesus
The first sight of a baby.

Paul Hepburn (10)
St Andrew's Primary School, Falkirk

Hallowe'en

It is midnight in the churchyard
As ghosts and ghouls emerge
Awakening the living dead
Hallowe'en is here.

Creaking coffins open on a night like this
Ready to send a greeting message
They'll send you a fright.

Dancing 'til the break of dawn
Flowing colours - red and fawn
Running back to their graves where they belong
So long ghouls.

Erin Vivers (10)
St Andrew's Primary School, Falkirk

A Spider's Web

A stoundingly beautiful

S mooth and delicate
P rey wanders unknowingly into the
I nsect trap
D elicate, handle with care
E lected for an arachnid's home
R ed with blood of victims past
S ilent, watching . . .

W eb in waiting
E legant in every way
B ait in the centre of the cunning trap.

Daniel McElroy (11)
St Andrew's Primary School, Falkirk

A Spider's Web

A rachnid's amazing work

S ticky trap sparkling in the night
P erfect in every way
I n the corner of the attic
D eath lies there in the darkness
E legantly made
R emarkable
S pinnaret of spinning silk

W iry dreamcatcher
E erie shape
B lood from victims in the past.

Jordan Cullen (11)
St Andrew's Primary School, Falkirk

A Spider's Web

A fragile web carefully built.

S pider returns to see what's been caught.
P erfectly set out his web lies empty.
I n the air it glides around.
D efinite to catch something in his web.
E xcellent in every way the spider is ready to catch his prey.
R eady he lies in wait.
S pider comes to his dinner.

W orth the wait, the web succeeded.
E verything is over until the next
B ait to be upon the spider's web.

Liam Casci (11)
St Andrew's Primary School, Falkirk

A Spider's Web

A rachnid's silky web

S parkling in the light
P atterned
I cy web
D azzling in a corner
E very web is fragile
R eflects in the sun
S ticky web

W onderful torture
E very web is like a snowflake
B eautiful web.

Laura Meade (11)
St Andrew's Primary School, Falkirk

A Spider's Web

A strange sight

S parkling in the morning dew
P erfectly formed
I n the corner of the garden
D aintily hanging in-between the flowers
E asily torn
R avishing
S himmering in the sunlight

W onderfully presented
E ffortlessly made
B rilliant in the moonlight

Rebeca Coll (11)
St Andrew's Primary School, Falkirk

A Spider's Web

A web glistening in the frost

S pinarets spin the sticky silk
P erching on the doors and walls
I n the corner can't be seen
D elicate silk
E tra bait for a trap
R adiant web sparkling in the sun
S parkling like a diamond

W iry dreamcatchers
E very moment out of sight
B eautiful, shaped like an octagon.

Dechlan Kearney (10)
St Andrew's Primary School, Falkirk

A Spider's Web

A snowflake of silky string

S himmering in the light
P erfect in every way
I n a corner it glistens
D elicate and fragile
E ight hairy legs feeling their way around
R emains there all day long
S parkling so bright

W iry dreamcatcher so very still
E xtremely beautiful
B urning in the light.

Rachel Graves (11)
St Andrew's Primary School, Falkirk

A Spider's Web

A net of silky thread

S pinning its web for hours
P roud of her web
I nsects caught in the web
D azzling in the light
E xcellent work
R ound and round she goes
S ticky patterns

W eb sticks to anything
E very web is fragile
B eautiful as can be.

Clare Davie (11)
St Andrew's Primary School, Falkirk

A Spider's Web

A shimmering snowflake made out of silk

S ticky but smooth, it glistens with frost
P roudly hanging
I n the corner of the doorway
D elicate and dripping with dew in the morning
E asy to break
R adiant when wet
S uspended between the door frame

W onderfully formed
E nticing insects
B eautiful and stunning.

Debbie So (11)
St Andrew's Primary School, Falkirk

The Blitz

Listening to the radio in my house,
I hear the high-pitched wail of the air raid siren,
My mum tells me to stay calm,
We put on our gas masks and run to the Anderson shelter,
In the Anderson shelter I can hear the droning of the German planes,
Wondering if my friends have been injured,
I feel I might not survive,
The drone is getting closer and closer,
The sound of the bombs is unbelievable,
Slowly the Stukas fly away,
The all-clear siren goes,
I have survived tonight.

Ryan Ferrie (11)
St Andrew's Primary School, Falkirk

Gran Poem

My gran is as beautiful as a bright red sunset.
Her hair is like a little kitten's beautiful grey fur.
Her eyes are like pretty sapphires that shine all day long.
Her face is like a bright sky.
When she walks she is like a really fast racing dog.
When she sits she is like a big teddy bear.
When she laughs she is like a really funny clown.
When she sleeps she is like an old steam train.
The best thing about my gran is she spoils me
with lots and lots of love.

Claire Louise Callaghan (9)
St Andrew's Primary School, Falkirk

The Blitz

The shrill of the siren woke us at night,
My family and I ran in fright,
We tried to keep calm although it was hard,
All in the Anderson shelter playing cards.
The sound of the doodlebugs' engines up high,
As the dogfights continued in the night sky,
Scared and shaking my mum sang a song
She said, 'Don't worry,' and 'you join along.'
I started to sing, to sing the song,
As the Germans dropped bomb after bomb.
It is now morning, the city is destroyed,
All of my family are very annoyed.

Hannah Kelly (11)
St Andrew's Primary School, Falkirk

Talking To People Who Live In The Dark

Blue is the cold feeling of going into the sea and playing in the waves.
Green is the smell of freshly cut grass.
Red is the feel of a blazing log fire.
White is the soft, cold feeling of sand on the seaside.
Silver is the sound of the clash of swords.

Liam Bruce (9)
St Andrew's Primary School, Falkirk

My World

I have a world with chocolate fountains,
With lollipops and ice cream mountains!
The walls are made of gingerbread brick,
The doors are made of candy-cane stick!

I have a world where it snows all the time,
And when I reach out for a snowflake I am on cloud nine!
I put on my scarf, my gloves and my hat,
I skate on the ice and sledge on my mat!

I love my world, though it makes me shiver,
To think, I own it forever and ever.
But when I wake up in the morning and find it's just a dream,
And just my imagination, no matter how real it may seem.
But then I can't get back no matter how hard I fight,
But I know I will revisit my world again tonight.

Nicole Linning
St Ninian's Primary School, Gourock

Tag You're It

I climbed the stairs with a feeling of dread,
I knew I did not want to go to bed.
I went to the bathroom to brush my teeth,
Went to bed, not knowing what was underneath!
I lay there in silence, there wasn't a sound,
Not even a grumble or footstep on the ground.

And then I heard a distant voice,
I knew I really had no choice.
As I stepped towards the door,
I knew that I'd soon be no more!
When I saw *it* I froze on the spot,
The room soon turned chilly, though it had been
                                            so very hot.

It came towards me, *it* was large and white,
It was terrifying especially in the middle of the night!
I felt a feeling in my stomach at the very pit,
Then *it* tapped me and cried, 'Tag you're it!'

Kathleen Isaac (11)
St Ninian's Primary School, Gourock

All About Golf

I like golf it's the best of all
I do what Donald says
With the ball
He puts me in the right position
He thinks I'm on a mission

I've got my bronze
It was a breeze
I would have got my silver
If I did not sneeze

I'll keep on trying
I won't give in
To miss out on gold
Would be a sin

I got my new club
With my Christmas money
I can't wait to give it a hit
The next time it is sunny

For Christmas I had a surprise
My sister got me a new putter
That opened my eyes

I put all my clubs
In my new bag
One person is jealous
And that's my dad!

Claire Urban (7)
St Paul's RC Primary School, Glenrothes

Milky Way

M illions of miles away
I n space
L ike a black hole
K ilometres wide with
Y ellow light in the middle.

W ouldn't eat it, if I were you!
A lmost out of the Earth's atmosphee
Y et it's beautiful to see.

Kieran Orr (8)
Springside Primary School, Irvine

Winter Poem

W arm in my house
I t is good to play in the snow
N o snowflake is the same
T he snow is cold
E ating soup keeps you cosy
R obins in my garden.

Kyle McLean (9)
Springside Primary School, Irvine

Stars

S parkly! It's those stars
T onight the sky is full of them
A ren't they bright like a torch
R eally sparkly, they are like diamonds
S leepy stars, it's time for bed.

Amy Kerr (8)
Springside Primary School, Irvine

The Hobby Horse

I had a little hobby horse
We galloped everywhere
All around the sitting room
And up and down the stair.
In and out the kitchen
And right across the hall
And when I galloped far too fast
Mum shouted, 'Watch out you don't fall!'

Holly Kirkpatrick (8)
Springside Primary School, Irvine

My Teddy

My teddy is cuddly and soft
I sleep with him every night
His bright eyes watch me wherever I go
His name is Broxy Bear.
He has parrot pyjamas, a cover
And a pillow for his head
He makes me feel so sleepy
When I take him up to bed.

Thomas Fletcher (8)
Springside Primary School, Irvine

My Cute Sister

My sister has just gone to nursery
She likes to paint
I am glad she likes it
She has lots of friends
My sister plays games
She cheats so she can win!
She is so much fun
I love her.

Paige Robertson (8)
Springside Primary School, Irvine

My Monkey

My monkey swings on the tree
He swings from branch to branch
He whistles and eats bananas
He jumps up and down
He is funny and silly
He says, *ah, ah, ah, ah*
And I laugh at him
He is furry
And he is small
And I love him to bits.

Leighanne Walker (8)
Springside Primary School, Irvine

My Snowman

I made a snowman
As perfect as can be
I took it in and
I made it some tea.
He burned his mouth!
Before he went to bed
I got him some pyjamas
Last night he went away
But first he wet the bed.

Daniel Key (8)
Springside Primary School, Irvine

Planets

Hard ground covered in craters
Aliens jumping out of holes
Freaky voices hooting in the air
Extremely excited because nobody has been here
Stars shining in space.

Jordan Mayes (9)
Stobhill Primary New Community School, Gorebridge

The Retired Greyhound

I am a greyhound,
I have bright eyes,
I am a dog,
Of a very large size.

The cockatiels tease me
For showing my ribs
But they have brains
Like my owners, like sieves.

I smell and see
Slops on the stove,
But of course
None are for me.

I used to run fast
Don't humans see?
Please just remember
It's not fair on me!

Caitlin Carr (10)
Stobhill Primary New Community School, Gorebridge

Sunshine

Sunglasses hanging from the tip of my nose
A chilling breeze running through my hair
Noisy children splashing in the deep swimming pool
Sunshine giving me a real superb tan!
Having a real cool barbecue at the beach
Getting a lovely massage by my father
Everyone singing songs before they leave

This is sunshine.

Stacey McCaig (9)
Stobhill Primary New Community School, Gorebridge

My Birthday

The 23rd June
I just can't wait,
'Cause on that day
It's my birthday.

I can just imagine
That huge chocolate cake,
With eleven candles
Just for me.

All those lovely presents
Wrapped in colourful paper,
With ribbons around the presents
I can imagine me opening them.

Oh when will that day come
I just can't wait,
23rd June
Hurry up and come.

Cheryl-Louise Burzynski (10)
Stobhill Primary New Community School, Gorebridge

Sunshine

There's people licking ice lollies,
There's seagulls gliding slowly past the boiling sun,
The sea sparkles so brightly,
The water is dripping down my face,
There's lots of people complaining because it's too hot,
There's children splashing in the sea,
I am longing for a freezing cold breeze.
I am getting into the car and the steering wheel is roasting,
It burns my hands.

This is sunshine.

Emily Lawrence (9)
Stobhill Primary New Community School, Gorebridge

Seasons

Leaves, leaves twirling around
Almost thrashing on the ground.

When the wind starts to howl
All the animals hurry and scowl.

As it's time for the snow to come
Go inside and warm your tum.

As the weather starts to change
It feels as if it's spring again.

Eventually it's summer, my favourite of them all
The butterflies, the insects come out and go to the mall.

But when it's time for the clocks to turn
The seasons begin with a churn.

Stacie Burgess (10)
Stobhill Primary New Community School, Gorebridge

Snow

I see snow falling softly from the midnight sky
Looping round and round.
I feel it landing gently on my face
The wind is freezing it's like an icicle
I feel like going to my friends
And having a snowball fight.

I smell some Christmas dinner
I look in a window,
A family is sitting at a warm fire,
I wish I was with my family at the fire.

Stephen Marshall (10)
Stobhill Primary New Community School, Gorebridge

A Windy Day

I hear the wind howling through the streets,
I feel it push me off my feet.
I see it shake the trees so tall,
I don't smell anything at all

The taste in my mouth was rough,
I thought, *I have to be tough.*
To survive the trials of,
This windy day.

Daniel Jack (10)
Stobhill Primary New Community School, Gorebridge

Sports Cars

I see big silver and gold alloys
I hear very loud revs on the racetrack
I wish I was one of the drivers
I feel the ground shaking
I touch the big, comfy seats.

This is a sports car.

Craig Rutherford (9)
Stobhill Primary New Community School, Gorebridge

Football

A man injured on a stretcher
Terrible tackle by Bobo Baldy
Great tackle by Neil Lennon
Amazing shot by John Hartson
Great goal by Larsson.

Ryan Gibson (9)
Stobhill Primary New Community School, Gorebridge

Sunshine

Hot blazing sun,
Wearing yellow shaded sunglasses,
Seagulls diving from the bright blue sky,
Touching the boiling sunbeds,
Sweating when sunbathing at the beach,
Ice-cold ice cream melting in my mouth,
Warm breeze flowing across my hair,
Sun twinkling on the warm sea,
Longing for a cool smooth wind.

Nicola Barclay (9)
Stobhill Primary New Community School, Gorebridge

Football

A poor tackle from Neil Lennon,
Loud cheer of a goal,
Fantastic goal from Henrik Larsson,
Brilliant penalty from Alan Thomson,
Size five ball wallops the post.

This is football.

William Urban (9)
Stobhill Primary New Community School, Gorebridge

Planets

I am strapped in a rocket blasting up to space
I thought I was floating in the planetary air
Getting out and seeing green, slimy Martians
Striding through volcanic dust
I hear the Martians babbling
I've landed on Mars and can feel the hard, cold rocks.

Steven Hogg (10)
Stobhill Primary New Community School, Gorebridge

Football

England are playing Finland in the World Cup and I am there.
A bad tackle from Paul Scholes and he got sent off.
A smashing goal from Michael Owen
A massive fight from both teams
The half-time whistle has blown
Now the teams are coming out
Yes another goal for England
Five more minutes to go
I know we are going to win
Just about to score and the full-time whistle goes
We see England lifting the World Cup.

Stephen Fraser (9)
Stobhill Primary New Community School, Gorebridge

Life

One life is something that happens along,
One life happens blink and it's gone,
Either way life goes on.

I hate my life,
It's all a big mess,
I'll always be afraid that you'll love me less,
My dreams have been shattered into a big pile,
But it all comes together when you smile.

Sean Allan (11)
Stobhill Primary New Community School, Gorebridge

Crocodile

My
pet
doesn't
have
wings
and
it
never
ever
sings.
Don't
suspect
a
nice
warm
smile
'cause
my
pet
is
a
crocodile!

William Wylie (11)
Thorn Primary School, Johnstone

My Pet Is?

My
pet
is
an
aardvark
it
does
not
bark
it
likes
to
sleep
in
the
dark.
My
pet
is
an
aardvark.

Stuart McCormick (10)
Thorn Primary School, Johnstone

My Pet

My
pet
is
the
best
pet
he
eats
the mouse
in
the
house
and
kills
the rats
under
the mats.
My
pet
is
a
cat.

Andrew Smith (11)
Thorn Primary School, Johnstone

Shark

My
favourite
animal
is
a
shark
it
does
not
beg
it
does
not
bark
because
my
pet
is
a
shark.

John Milligan (11)
Thorn Primary School, Johnstone

Eel

My
Animal
Is
An
Eel
For
His
Meal
It's
Got
To
Be
Real
That's
The
Deal
About
My
Eel.

Alan Smith (10)
Thorn Primary School, Johnstone

Giraffe

My
favourite
animal
is
a
giraffe.
He
eats
leaves
from
high
trees
and
doesn't
laugh.

Gary Bull (11)
Thorn Primary School, Johnstone

Braces

I know I'm getting braces,
For a year or two.
You may wish for them,
But for me it's really true.

A pretty painful period,
With teeth extractions too.
Four teeth altogether,
Each time removing two.

With very careful brushing
And visits to you know who,
My teeth will be straightened
So I can smile beautifully at you.

Nichola Philp (11)
Uplawmoor Primary School, Glasgow

The Serengeti

A thousand miles from here or more,
Reptiles rule the safari floor.
With snakes and lizards, all scaly things,
Scuttling about amongst hairy kings.

A thousand miles from here or more,
Small mammals cry for their mums who are no more.
Bleating for their fathers too,
Next time maybe it will be you.

A thousand miles from here or more,
Cheetahs, lions, tigers all seem to love blood and gore.
Clawing, ripping, tearing, shredding,
This is a very sad ending to a poor animal's life.

But who are we to criticise?
In every country lives are sacrificed
In wars about politics and religion
This is one thing we don't have to go
A thousand miles or more for.

David Ross Paterson (11)
Uplawmoor Primary School, Glasgow

The Park

I go to the park with my friends
We swing on the swings and go down the slide
The swings feel like a roller coaster ride!
I am walking to the park with my friend
As we are running to the swings I trip
And fall flat on my face!
My friend falls over me
We laugh and make our way to the swings.
They creak and crack as we swing.
I go to the park with my friends
We swing on the swings and go down the slide
The swings feel like a roller coaster ride!
Oh how I love the park!

Laura Wood (11)
Uplawmoor Primary School, Glasgow

My Poem

My poem is quite short,
But longer than a piglet's snort,
Longer than a dog's bark,
But shorter than a day at the park.

My poem is not too hard,
But you must always be on your guard.
This poem is not too easy,
But it won't make you feel queasy.

My poem won't take up much time,
And hopefully it will rhyme.
So stay on your guard,
Because it might be hard.
Here's hoping I didn't waste
Your time!

Laura McMurdo (11)
Uplawmoor Primary School, Glasgow

Mr Santa Claus

Mr Claus is everyone's best friend,
Getting letters as long as songs.
His nine reindeer all in a line,
Dropping presents from up high,
Down chimneys all night long.

In his Toyland palace warm,
He watches you,
He watches me.
On a special, family loving day,
Opening packages,
Rummaging in stockings,
Screaming loud and long . . .
Thank you Mr Santa Claus.

Caroline Nicol (11)
Uplawmoor Primary School, Glasgow

Overboard

'Man overboard!'
Called the crew
I said, 'Who's going to save him?'
They all shouted, 'You!'

I swam and swam
Until my arms were numb
And then in the distance
I saw my chum.

He was bobbing up,
He was bobbing down.
Then all of a sudden
'Argh!'
I'm going to drown!

Jonathan Dawson-Bowman (11)
Uplawmoor Primary School, Glasgow

My Brother

My brother is as slow as a snail,
My brother is a pest,
But when you give him some sweets,
He is quiet as a mouse.

My brother is as noisy as a crowd,
Watching a pop band live,
But when he gets chocolate,
He is quiet and not so loud.

My brother is nice,
But not so good looking,
Should I keep my brother?
Or do you want him?

Jessica Strang (10)
Uplawmoor Primary School, Glasgow

Saturday

My cousins came at 8 o'clock,
While I was watching Rock,
After that we went outside to play
And I was the catcher when we played sixty.
Then we went up to my room
And when we shut the door it went *boom!*
We played together quite a lot,
We also made large clay pots.
When we were putting our PJs on,
Emma took so very long.
But Trish and I were as fast as lightning,
In bed we did a little writing
And then we went to sleep,
        Night, night.

Isla Erskine (10)
Uplawmoor Primary School, Glasgow

A Fly

Fly, fly, little fly,
Don't go on the window sill,
You might be squashed
Like your Uncle Bill.

Fly, fly, little fly,
By and by you fly,
You dart around
Like a bit of rubber
That's been thrown
In class.

Ben Rodger (11)
Uplawmoor Primary School, Glasgow

My Best Friend

My best friend Hazel is the best,
She is better than all the rest.
We go shopping, swimming and we even dance,
It's funny when Hazel starts to prance.
When we have sleepovers we always stay up late,
I think she's totally great.
When she smiles she's as bright as the sun,
Both of us have a bunch of fun.
We say words at the same time,
You may call it a twin thing, we like to rhyme.
Hazel and I always have a good giggle,
Now that is what I call my best friend.

Alison Macleod (11)
Uplawmoor Primary School, Glasgow

Football

F irst football match I went to see
O n a cold and frosty Saturday,
O ver the net went the ball,
T errible miss was said by all.
B est match I have ever been to see
A nd at half-time we had a cup of tea.
L ast few moments of the game,
L eft hand winger scored again.

Angus Erskine (11)
Uplawmoor Primary School, Glasgow

Me

My hair is as blonde as straw,
My eyes are as blue as the sea,
My mum said I am as tall as a mountain
And that describes me.

Jessica Maycock (11)
Uplawmoor Primary School, Glasgow

Beware The Orcs

Orcs sleep anywhere
Orcs sleep everywhere
Orcs are really ugly
Well maybe some are not
But if they don't get enough food
They can be very rude.
If the Easter bunny happens by,
They will steal his eggs from under his eye
Although they think this is quite funny
Try telling that to Mr Bunny.

Joi Dinsmor (10)
Uplawmoor Primary School, Glasgow

At The Stables

When you go to the stables,
You'd better watch out,
You're handed a special hat, like hard, frozen plums,
The horses are waiting and standing tall,
Just waiting for you to jump up and fall,
Their jackets are heavy, the saddle is too,
So when you go to the stables, watch out for the poo!

When it comes to 4pm you hear a soft neigh,
You know they are sleeping and bid them good day.

Gemma Egan (10)
Uplawmoor Primary School, Glasgow

My Little Puppy

My little puppy all soft and fluffy
She leaps like a lamb and she can't stay calm
She greets you with a stick that's big and thick
She's also gentle, sometimes goes mental.

Sarah Addie (10)
Uplawmoor Primary School, Glasgow

My Family

My dad can be grumpy
But tries to be kind,
He's someone you can talk to
I do find.

My mum, she gives me cuddles
When I'm feeling down
And when I was little she
Swung me round and round.

My big sister is really cool,
But has to catch an early bus
Before I go to school.

One of my little brothers
Is a real big pest
But very, very rarely
He can be the best.

My youngest little brother
Was the last of us to be born,
It may sound very strange,
But he likes peas, beans and corn.

Now you've met my family,
Come and meet my pets,
Perhaps you'd better not, you say,
Or it may be you at the vet's!

Lucy Morrant (10)
Uplawmoor Primary School, Glasgow

Dolphins

Dolphins are great animals to see,
Jumping six feet in the air,
Splashing like mad,
Which I wouldn't dare.

Dolphins are the most fun animals in the sea,
I don't know about you but they are for me,
There are many types with each a special name,
But each type love to splash and play a game.

Naomi Dawson-Bowman (11)
Uplawmoor Primary School, Glasgow

I Wish I Was . . .

I wish I was an astronaut, flying round and round.
I wish I was a fisherman, casting all my nets.
I wish I was a lifeguard, saving all my friends.
I wish I was a tourist, touring the Earth.
But sadly I'm just me!

I wish I was an actor, making lots of money.
I wish I was a hairdresser, cutting people's hair.
I wish I was a policeman, breaking up the crowds
I wish I was a football player, scoring lots of goals
I wish I was a falconer, saving birds of prey
But I'm just me!

But I am a basketball player, playing with my team.
But I am an actor, stealing every scene.
But I am a drummer, drumming is such fun.
But I am a child, playing in the sun
I'm probably better being me!

Jordan Moir (11)
Wallacestone Primary School, Falkirk

Life Is Fun For An Alien

Life is fun for an alien
Living on planet Earth
To try and act like human beings
To copy and study their feelings

Life is funny on Earth
The way humans talk
They open a hole in their faces
And then some sound comes out!

Lunchtimes are always fun
To watch humans eat
When they pick up their food
With a little pointy stick
And chew it with their teeth

Humans are strange
Their eyes leak
When they are sad
Or have been bad

Planet Earth is a strange place
But I'll recommend it
For a first time buyer's case.

Amy Tucker (12)
Wallacestone Primary School, Falkirk

Oh Car!

Oh Car you take me everywhere even underwater.
Oh Car you pick me up from every club.
Oh Car you are my number one.
Oh Car you are my pride and joy.
Oh Car you can fly like the wind.
Oh Car you can win every race.

Daniel Struthers (10)
Wallacestone Primary School, Falkirk

Life Is Fun

The Joy Of My Life

As I walk towards the stable
the flood of happiness runs through my veins.
I dream of riding off and down the winding country lanes.

As I reach the stable door,
I hear the joyous cry.
It's coming from behind the bars,
where my friends must lie.

As I step into the gloom,
a curious head turns to see.
The eyes, deep and dark,
full of love and faith for me.

As I talk to him sweetly,
I tell him why I love to ride.
I love it when he canters me away
and takes all the pain from inside.

As I reach and touch his face,
my hurt begins to melt.
He lets me climb onto his back,
and he senses how I feel.

As I cling onto his black mane
and he nuzzles me.
I smell his sweet chestnut coat
and he sets me free.

Laura Henderson (12)
Wallacestone Primary School, Falkirk

Life Is Fun

When I wake up in the morning,
I pick up a book with my hands,
For I find it fun to read,
And travel to faraway lands.

I imagine that I am there,
And doing the things that the characters do,
Being like a wizard or a dragon,
Or stealing some treasure from you!

I like reading books like 'The Hobbit',
And 'The Lord Of The Rings' is good too,
For people like elves and hobbits,
Can have much more fun than me or you!

Life is so great,
When you can become someone else,
It gets boring again,
When you go back to yourself.

Jennifer Sneddon (11)
Wallacestone Primary School, Falkirk

Life Is Fun

Life is fun being a computer,
Seeing all the faces ranging gold, bronze and pewter.
Life is fun being a computer,
Seeing all the faces some lovely, some quite ugly.
Life is fun being a computer,
Giving information to those who are on me for a caper.
Life is fun being a computer,
Seeing all the people scream and shout in my face.
Life is fun being a computer,
Waiting to see what they'll do.
Life is fun being a computer,
Being shut down to sleep at night.

Richard Fairgrieve
Wallacestone Primary School, Falkirk

Toy Dog

Oh Toy Dog, my number one.
The best person to have for fun.
Though you have twins and brothers
The same as you
If you were just alive,
I would never feel blue.

You dogs, who are wonderful pairs
The shame is that you can't speak,
That I think is unfair.
Travelling very long to your doggy school
If it's silly, I think it's so cool.

Playing and texting on your mobile phone
In some other things that deserves a bone.
You're so cuddly in every way
I will take you everywhere for a walk each day.

Cameron Dick (10)
Wallacestone Primary School, Falkirk

Life Is Fun

Life is fun
When we kick a ball and run
Sharing and caring, getting wet and being daring.
Playing with our friends
And drawing with our pens.
Life is fun outside
When we play seek and hide,
Dressing up, playing games also having nicknames,
Having pets
Catching tadpoles with our nets.
Oh how life is fun
And for me it's just begun.

Amy Thomson (11)
Wallacestone Primary School, Falkirk

Mum

Oh Mum,
I love you so,
Oh Mum,
I hope you know
How much I love you, Oh!

Oh Mum,
I hope you like
The mint chocolate
I bought last night,
The box is coloured the bright blue of your eyes.

Oh Mum,
The food you cook is yummy,
You always make the house sparkle,
My bed is always cosy,
And your cuddles are warm.

Abigail Field (10)
Wallacestone Primary School, Falkirk

Life Is Fun

I enjoy playing with friends,
Playing and playing until the day ends,
I like playing the computer and the Xbox,
And then at the beach I climb up tall rocks.
Life is fun playing Simpsons' Hit and Run,
I like going bowling, scoring a strike.
There are still many more things that I like,
I like going swimming in the pool,
Also being educated at the school,
I like to ride my bike,
While my little brother goes on a trike.
Life is fun, life is fun,
Playing in the shining sun.

Christopher Lenathen (11)
Wallacestone Primary School, Falkirk

My Family

My mum is funny
She dances like a clown
She is funny like money
she has brown eyes
She works in the Bingo
And she has to singo.
she has black hair
And likes to eat ice poles.

My mum nearly set my fish's tail on fire
It was funny because my mum was drunk,
My dad said that it was a prank.

My mum and dad sent me to bed
I went to sleep and in the morning
I had fun and I got a bun.
At night I always have a bath
And we always have a laugh.

Liam Park (7)
Wallacestone Primary School, Falkirk

Life Is Fun

Life is fun when we go down the burn,
to catch tadpoles, newts and toads.
Life is fun when we go down the burn,
to build dens out of wood and metal.
Life is fun when we go down the burn,
to climb trees and jump in the burn.
Life is fun when we go down the burn,
we make swords out of sticks and
spearheads out of flint.
Life is fun when we go down the burn,
we make swings out of rope and
hang them from trees.
Life is fun down the burn!

Ellis Robert Main (11)
Wallacestone Primary School, Falkirk

My Favourite Toy

I have a toy
I have a cuddly toy
I play with him all day
I take him everywhere with me
He is small and fat and spotty.

He has brown eyes
He has got black and white fur,
My toy is sad all the time
My toy is cute and he is mine
We play games everywhere.

We play funny games
We play mad games
We play glad games
One time he hit me
Then he cuddles me.

He comes to bed with me.
We sleep all night
We play all night
I love him.

Gillian Anderson (7)
Wallacestone Primary School, Falkirk

Life Is Fun

I like to play the piano to annoy the neighbours below.
I like to play with my friends and to roll about in the snow.
I like to relax on the beach, so I might be able to get some peace.
I like it when Christmas comes and a brand new year begins.
I like it on my birthday when I get lots of money to spend.
If you have lots of money the fun will never end.
I like it when my parents tell me I have a heart of gold.
I think you should ask my teacher, who only looks twenty years old.
I would like it if my teacher would agree,
That no one is as well-behaved as me!

Debbie Marshall
Wallacestone Primary School, Falkirk

Laggan The Menace

Laggan the menace
Is a little Dennis
He runs and runs
For miles and never stops.

He slides on the mop
He jumps on my bed
And then he drops
On the little socks.

He is a little Dennis
My little menace
His little legs
Are getting tired.

He runs to his basket
Falls asleep
He looks as cuddly
As a sheep.

Katie Anderson (7)
Wallacestone Primary School, Falkirk

Life Is Fun

Life is fun when we laugh and have fun.
Going to the pics and eating pick 'n' mix
Swimming a length, push-ups with strength
Playing in the sun is oh such fun.
Listening to CDs and watching DVDs,
A shopping spree and running free.
Texting friends and drawing with pens,
Going to parties and eating Smarties
Going to the park till the sky turns dark.

Allyson Eadie
Wallacestone Primary School, Falkirk

Dad

Oh Dad you're so friendly
Oh Dad you're so great
Oh Dad you make me laugh
Oh Dad you're so caring
Oh Dad you're the best.
Oh I love hearing your jokes
Dad you give me joy
Oh Dad you're the best.

I always think of you when I'm in my bed
I will always appreciate you Dad,
You're the best.

Oh Dad you are going to be No.1
Oh Dad you love your cars
I love you Dad, I always will.

Sean Blair (10)
Wallacestone Primary School, Falkirk

Mum

Oh Mum,
You are always there for me,
Oh Mum,
You are the best.

You are very good at gardening,
Planting flowers and little trees.
Oh Mum gardening is your thing!

Oh Mum,
Your little black car is so shiny,
You drive it everywhere.

Oh Mum,
You are always caring for me,
You are the best mum.

Rachel Peggie (10)
Wallacestone Primary School, Falkirk

My Best Friends

Oh all my best friends,
You are such fun,
You are all number one!
Raisha Ahmed, you are so kind,
You bring me happiness to more than my mind.
Rachel Peggie, even though you are afraid of spiders,
You always listen to my problems
That's why you're like six giant binders.
Rachel Knight, I know you like S'Club 8 ,
That's why we're always in a debate!

Oh all my best friends
You are number one,
You look wonderful!
Raisha Ahmed, your gorgeous eyelashes flicking away,
It reminds me of your beautiful hair that you have every day.
Rachel Peggie with your hair so black and your eyes so green.
I want to shout out *mean* but I'm not keen.
Rachel Knight, your lovely blonde hair makes me care
And your nice green eyes makes me feel like a queen!

Oh all my best friends,
Your are all number one,
We always have fun!
Rachel Peggie, your favourite game is the sign,
Even though you have to wait in line.
Rachel Knight your favourite game is races,
And you run several paces.
Raisha Ahmed your favourite game is football,
And you always beat them all!

Suzanne Smith (10)
Wallacestone Primary School, Falkirk

Mobile Phone

Oh Mobile Phone,
As great as can be,
Always there by me.

I look at you with happiness,
As you shine with glee,
And you will be colourful.

Mobile Phone as I hold you in my hand,
With tightness,
The smoothness in my hands.

I use you every night, my fingers fiddling as I text,
The games I play on you rock as I compete against other people.

When people phone me I hear the Nokia tune,
I don't answer because I love the tune,
Oh Mobile Phone, Oh Mobile Phone,
You will always stay next to me.

Dawn Sharp (10)
Wallacestone Primary School, Falkirk

Game Boy

Oh Game Boy you're my favourite toy,
Every day I have hours of joy.
I love your light, it's so big and bright,
When I'm playing in the night.

You feel so smooth, so red and bright,
You are so small and close, so tight.
Your buttons are very small,
Even though I'm so tall.

I have specially bought some games for you,
Poke'mon Ruby and the Sims too.
I'd take you everywhere I go,
But my mum always says, *'No!'*

Robbie Cochrane (10)
Wallacestone Primary School, Falkirk

Winnie The Pooh

Oh Winnie the Pooh,
You know that I love you,
You are all my joy,
And all my pride,
All the time you are by my side.

You are my best friend,
You know our friendship will never end,
I always know you are near,
You are bold without any fear.

You cuddle me at night,
When I am lonely or if I have a fright.
You might be small and tubby,
But you have the biggest heart ever.

We will be friends forever and ever,
Our friendship will end, never.

Holly Stevenson (10)
Wallacestone Primary School, Falkirk

My Bedroom

Oh Bedroom, Oh Bedroom, mine you'll always be,
You're cosy and colourful, you're always there for me.
You're fun to be with, all your toys are too,
Oh Bedroom, Oh Bedroom, how fantastic are you?

Oh Bedroom, Oh Bedroom, so are all your friends,
Mrs Hairbrush, Mr Hairbrush and all their little friends.
My favourite colour is yellow and that's the colour of you,
The television, Oh it is so cool, it's loud and colourful,
A bit like you.

Oh Bedroom, Oh Bedroom, I will never leave you!

Katie Hunter (10)
Wallacestone Primary School, Falkirk

Bugsy

Oh Bugsy,
You're my favourite soft toy.
Oh Bugsy I don't know if you're a girl or a boy.
Oh Bugsy,
Many nights I've spent dreaming with you.
Oh Bugsy,
I don't know what I'd do without you.

Oh Bugsy,
You're there when I'm feeling glum.
Oh Bugsy,
Everyone loves you, including my mum.
Oh Bugsy,
You're soft and furry.
Oh Bugsy,
You stay clean so we don't have to worry.

Oh Bugsy,
You're not too tall.
Oh Bugsy,
You're not too small.
Oh Bugsy,
You're like a real pet.
Oh Bugsy,
But you don't need the vet.

Victoria Fordham (10)
Wallacestone Primary School, Falkirk

My Best Friend

Oh Rosie you are there for me,
my best friend you will always be.
Rosie you give me joy and pride,
you are always right by my side.

Your eyes are greeny-brown,
I hardly ever see you frown.
You have browny-blonde hair,
to me you are always very fair.
You have freckles on your face,
no one could ever take your place.
You have purple glasses,
as well as long eyelashes.

Oh Rosie you love to shop,
you also love to bop.
You like to swim,
nothing in your life is dim.
You have two dogs,
you always wear the trendiest togs.

Oh Rosie you are the number one friend,
Oh Rosie you love to bend.
Oh Rosie, Oh Rosie you are my best friend,
I am so lucky to have you as my best friend.

Suzy Camlin (10)
Wallacestone Primary School, Falkirk

My Little Rabbits

I love my pet rabbits, so cuddly and soft,
I love the way they look
My darlings I love.
I love you pet rabbits
And I like you, you know.

They always eat lettuce and salad
You must know
Rabbit are hard to clean out.
My mum thinks they are stinking
But I do not.

They are covered in patches, black and white
I have to clean them out every night
They are sometimes frightened of some odd people
A nuisance you know
I just know they are beautiful.

Stefanie Eadie (7)
Wallacestone Primary School, Falkirk

PS2

Oh PS2, Oh PS2 I really adore you,
You're my pride and joy, my favourite toy.

You look so smooth, so shiny and black,
I enjoy playing you in the dark.

The texture you have is so bumpy
And when I play you I feel so happy.

The use of you is so great,
I have so many games to play.

You also play DVDs
And I have plenty.

Aaron Lawrie (10)
Wallacestone Primary School, Falkirk

Oh Eeyore

Oh Eeyore, Oh Eeyore,
You're as cute as can be.
Whenever I need you,
You're always there for me.

Oh Eeyore, Oh Eeyore,
You're my No.1,
You're always up to having some fun.
Whenever I'm upset or down in the dumps,
You're always there to cheer me up.

Oh Eeyore, Oh Eeyore,
I love you so much,
You're always there to give me a hug.

Rachel Bett (10)
Wallacestone Primary School, Falkirk

Mobile Phone

Oh Mobile Phone, you are such fun,
I could listen to your tones all day long.
I have taken a photo of a hot cross bun,
Oh 02X1 you are the one.

I have got to level 2 on mini golf,
I love texting, even at night.
My mum tells me to switch it off,
I text, no not now, having lots of fun.

Wake up, wake up.
Phew! Only a dream.

Scott Kenny (10)
Wallacestone Primary School, Falkirk

Finn

Oh . . . Finny Winny,
You're my dog
Your fur's so soft
Your tail's so small
Your nose, so wet
I love them all!

Oh . . . Finny Winny,
You're my dog
Your funny face
Your silly toys
Your floppy ears
They're all my joys!

Oh . . . Finny Winny,
You're my dog
Your puppy eyes
Your muddy paws
And with your big appetite
There isn't any food left in sight!

Oh . . . Finny Winny,
You're my dog
You're so great
You're the best ever mate!

Caitlin Genoe (10)
Wallacestone Primary School, Falkirk

My Family

My brother is a menace
He is very, very mad
Whenever he sees a toy car
He'll ask, 'Can I have that Dad?'
Dad will say, 'No, let's go back to the car.'
On the way back to the car
We meet my sister
'Ha! Ha! Got you, watch out it's dark!
Watch out wherever you park.'

My mum is quite tall
So is my sister
And Dad, my brother and I are really quite small.
We all have dark brown hair
My mum, sister, brother and I have brown eyes
My dad has green eyes.

When my brother is cold
He'll shout 'Mummy put the heating on.'
'What is the magic word?'
'Please,' he would say.

I love everyone in my family
I love to hear my brother say this.
Mum's calling. Oh I've got to go. Cheerio!

Karen Brown (7)
Wallacestone Primary School, Falkirk

My Best Friend Karen

She's small, she's cute
My best friend Karen
Her short brown hair
Is very fair.

Her funny jokes
Make me laugh a lot
So I tell her,
'Tell me a little more.'

We will always be together
Forever, me and Karen
She's smart, Karen
And I know she will always be that way.

Cara MacLure (7)
Wallacestone Primary School, Falkirk

My Puppy Dog Milo

I love my pet, my cute little pet.
It goes in its bed and it lies.
He has four little paws and a cute little nose.

He plays with his toys, goes with a noise.
I love him so sweetly
I love him with care, please let me keep him.
I love him better than my bear.

So I kept him
I love him
I love, love him
But I hate this goat, he stinks!
Oh well, who cares!

Charlie Watters (7)
Wallacestone Primary School, Falkirk

Game Boy

My Game Boy's such fun
That I play all day long
And in the morning sun
The game is Ruby.

I am Andy
Who eats lots of candy
The game makes funny noises
With different funny noises that is.

I play till it is time to go out
Today is different,
We are going out all day
First, swimming then McDonald's
And at last, my Gran's, to play.

She lives far away,
That was the day
Away from home.
I didn't play much with my Game Boy.

Andrew Richard Mackenzie (7)
Wallacestone Primary School, Falkirk

My Elephant

I wish I had an elephant to call my very own
He would be called Anthony
But I would call him Tone.

I would keep him in the garden
Tied to a cherry tree
When I came home from school
He would come running up to me.

He'd have a long, skinny trunk
And two big flapping ears
I am eight just now
And I would keep him for fifty years.

Calum Wood (8)
Wallacestone Primary School, Falkirk

Tae A Chicken Satay

As a wait tae stairt the buffet,
A get mair an mair anxious,
A stairt tae shudder,
A jist cannae wait,
A jump up an' charge,
Like a leopard huntin' its prey,
I look an' nearly faint,
Far there it is thon lovely chicken satay.

A handle it so gentle still,
An tak that single bite,
A taste o delight in every bite,
that's whit it's like tae me,
As its tender inside is gettin' pished abute,
A suddenly feel it at the back o ma throat,
It's very like a fight for life,
Its final fight is lost,
It fas doon the waterfaw and faws to its doom.

Whar its pals ill join it far their doom,
At the waterfaw's bottom room.

Kevin Purves (11)
Wallacestone Primary School, Falkirk

My Guinea Pig

Pumpkin is a guinea pig
With orange hair like a wig.
With little black beady eyes
And a loud squeak is how he cries.
A twitching nose that he sniffs for food
He would eat all day if he could.

Laura Findlay (8)
Wallacestone Primary School, Falkirk

To A Chip . . .

Your delightful aroma drifts past me,
It drives me into the kitchen to see,
I race out my room,
Smoke erupts from the chip pan with a boom,
Suddenly all goes silent as if I was in a sunken boat,
Then I see you lying there in your crispy golden coat.

I pour on you a red sea of sauce,
I'll show you who's the boss,
I take my time,
You taste so fine,
And in less than a second you're mine.

I look around for more chips to eat,
You'll go with anything, even meat,
But then it strikes me you are no more,
Neither is the sauce I took time to pour,
But when I recover, I have a comforting thought,
Next Friday, lots more chips will be bought.

Julie Duffy (11)
Wallacestone Primary School, Falkirk

My Hamster

I have a hamster called Minx
she has big black eyes that never blink.
Her fur is the colour of honey
and is supersoft like a bunny.
She chews her cage bars
which is quite funny
And she cost a lot of money.
Her favourite food is cheese
and has a jar where she wees.

Stuart Brooks (8)
Wallacestone Primary School, Falkirk

My Imaginary Friend

I have a horse that no one can see,
But no one even believes me,
My friends all think that I am one big laugh,
Because of my horse called Kath.

Ok, she could be fake,
She can't be!
Because she had some of my cake,
She can't be!
Because she drank all of my Coke.

Soon I found she was all in my head,
I found out when I was tucked up in bed,
After Mum came through to say, 'Goodnight'
I looked out of the window and got such a fright,
There was nothing there.

I thought our friendship would never end,
But everyone was right, she was my imaginary friend.

Jade Law (11)
Wallacestone Primary School, Falkirk

The Hamster

It is furry, it is white,
and it doesn't always sleep at night!

It lives in a cage, it doesn't get out.
If it did it would run about.

It is small, it is thin,
and it eats from a little tin.

I wish I had this hamster, it really would be good.
If I did have it, I would feed it lots of food!

Philip Campbell (8)
Wallacestone Primary School, Falkirk

My Cool Friend

Her eyes are as green as the sea,
her hair is as gold as can be.
At drawing she is better
but not at letter
and that's why she likes me.

I liked it when we made a den,
she pretended to be a hen.
She is so funny,
especially when she spilt the honey!

She is the best in every way,
So I play with her every day!

I write this poem,
not for the world arena,
But I write this for Catriona!

Emily Deans (8)
Wallacestone Primary School, Falkirk

My Best Friend

My friend's name is Charmaine
She has yellow hair and blue eyes.
She is funny and cute.

She goes to dancing
And is very good
For Charmaine, she likes doing the splits.

I like playing with her
In the summer we like to play on swings
And have dinner.

Linsey Robertson (7)
Wallacestone Primary School, Falkirk

My Funny Fish

This is my fish
He lives in a dish
He is very orange
He has lots of horns.

He spins round and round
In his big tank
And he thanks all the people he meets
And he likes playing football in his tank.

He likes chips too!
Sometimes he gets washed down the loo.
Where he goes I go too
So now you know about him too.

Caitlin Riach (7)
Wallacestone Primary School, Falkirk

My Best Friend

She's very big, her name's Samantha.
She likes to run, I like her very much.
But I've got friends at school.
I play with her at the weekends.

She laughs when I tickle her
And doesn't tickle me.
In the morning we play mums and dads.
We go and eat our crisps and munch
And in a bunch for our lunch.
She loves ducks in the pond.

Gail Scobbie (7)
Wallacestone Primary School, Falkirk

My Funny Friend

He like to play football
And he tackles people
But he's not good in goal.

And he's very good at football
But not as good as me
And Darren.

And he likes to play
And run around the playground
Playing tig.

And I have been to his house
And he has one fish
And its name is Nemo.

Tony Jakub (7)
Wallacestone Primary School, Falkirk

My Best Friend Charmaine

She is very cute and has eyes like the sea.
She is very cuddly and wonderful to see.

She has yellow hair and she is tall
She is thin and as beautiful as anyone.

I like her very much
Because she's very kind to me.

She is great and brainy
And she's the best friend anyone could have.

Amelia Watson (7)
Wallacestone Primary School, Falkirk

To My Friendly Polar Bear

I went into my bathroom,
I found my big polar bear,
It said something, who was that?
It said, 'Who are you?'
I heard it again.
I soon found out it was a polar bear.
I soon jumped into my full hot bath,
My silly white polar bear jumped in
My little sister came in and said that it was a fake.
But the polar bear said, 'Hi how are you?'
Charlotte replied, 'Hi, I'm fine.'
My dad came and said, 'Why are you playing
with your polar bear?'
The polar bear said, 'Hi, how are you?'
Dad replied, 'Hi, I'm fine.'
My mum came in and said the same.
'Where will we keep Polar?
Can we keep him in the bath,
Or can we keep him in the swimming pool,
In the back garden,
And can we take it on holiday,
Can we take it to see Gran
And Granma and Auntie Louise,
And everyone in the family,
And can I ask some of my friends
And can we take it to the shops,
Even in the snow or rain?'
I can take it down to Gran's
If it's windy or not.
I went into the bathroom,
And Polar was gone forever and ever.

Julia Downes (10)
Wallacestone Primary School, Falkirk

The Five-Day Corned Beef Dreamer

To corned beef, how I dream of you every day.

On Monday morning I dream of what I will have for my tea
maybe corned beef with creamy potatoes
and a blanket of cheese sauce.

At Tuesday playtime I dream of what my loving tea will be
maybe smooth corned beef with bread as white as snow
and crispy fried potatoes.

Wednesday afternoon and here I go again
I dream of corned beef.
I think I'll have toast, as crunchy as a Crunchie,
some juicy beans and . . . corned beef.

Thursday night, when I am playing football
the dream kicks in again.
Tonight *hmm*, succulent cheesy macaroni with the usual . . . corned
beef.

Friday night as I walk home from school
I have a feeling I'm getting corned beef.
As I open the front door I try to smell corned beef.
No.
I open the kitchen door and right before me is
mince and tatties!
No!

Corned beef, corned beef, where would I be
if you weren't between my teeth?

Ewan Baird (11)
Wallacestone Primary School, Falkirk

To A Double Double Pizza

As my mum phones from work
Asking what I want for tea,
I say, 'Double, double pizza please.'
It simply is exquisite.

As my mum says, 'Yes.'
I simply say, 'Yippee!'
Then when she gets off the phone
I jump the walls with glee.

As I sit down
And wait twenty minutes
My tummy starts to rumble
It knows no limits.

As my mum
Comes through the door
And cuts up my
Double double pizza, oh what galore.

When I smell that mouth-watering smell
I jump up from the chair
And run through to the kitchen
There's no time to stop and stare.

And there it is in all its glory
Sitting on its plate
I grasp it with my hands
Ready to meet its fate.

I lift it up towards my mouth
I sink my teeth into its skin
I rip away its little dress
With all its polka dots.

And this sadly is the end
For our little friend
But don't cry
Maybe you'll meet one next week.

Jennifer Anderson (11)
Wallacestone Primary School, Falkirk

For The Silvery Lake In Congo

The silvery lake in Congo
Beside where the poorest lived,
Would you not think they'd be fortunate,
With the treasure from the lake that could be sieved?

For a troll guarded the plank, the entrance to the cavern,
Beneath the silky waters lay a pile of gems just for taking.
No, oh no, that is not what they're for, as the legend's told,
These gems are far too priceless, certainly not to be sold!

The legend has it that anyone who enters
Should not, would not, could not turn back.
The human has been touched by the curse.
Curse of the angelic water fairies who are in favour of a snack!

But in the creepy moonlight
More creatures are unearthed
To keep the peace in all of the land.
Or just to lend a hand!

These centaurs, scorpicors, imps and gargoyles too
Are not at all in the least bit mean or scary
As a matter of fact they could be your best mates,
They really wouldn't hurt a fly, neither would the fairies!

So why can't the gems be removed?
They say they are bewitched!
Everyone gets confused,
Tourists do come that is true but no one really can be sure,
If it was just a folk tale from one old man . . .
In Congo!

Mhairi de Sainte Croix (11)
Wallacestone Primary School, Falkirk

To A Fruit Salad

To a fruit salad,
For you I wrote this special ballad!
We're waiting at the table, finishing the main course,
Mum is in the kitchen,
Chopping with great force!

The smells are wafting through the door,
Waiting for the next dish can be such a bore!
Oranges, bananas, apples, grapes,
All different sizes and shapes.
Kiwis, cherries, strawberries too,
Blackberries make my lips turn blue!

There they are, sitting on my plate,
Unaware of their impending fate!
Sweet and crunchy,
Juicy and munchy,
all chopped up in a bowl.
Oh how I wish, oh how I wish,
That I could just swallow you whole!
The smell of apples newly ripe,
Granny Smith, Mackintosh, whatever the type.
Or the fragrance of the strawberries,
Topped with cream,
For some, a dream!

For the fruits the journey awaits,
Starting at my very plate,
The fork goes down and then I spear,
The others wait in mortal fear!

The taste is exquisite,
Fit for a queen on her royal visit.
This would make the perfect dish,
But first you'd have to have the classic,
Chips and fish!

So you can keep
Your ice cream and jelly,
Because I prefer fruit
In my belly!

Hannah Deans (11)
Wallacestone Primary School, Falkirk

To A Pepperoni Pizza

To a pepperoni pizza on a Friday night,
It's my favourite, what a delight,
My tastebuds tingle as I walk down the hall,
Whenever I have pepperoni pizza I run up the wall.

When it's being cooked,
I have to have a look,
And wait with anticipation,
My mum says we eat so much pizza
We could feed the nation.

As the spicy sausage sizzles and fries,
I can't quite believe my eyes,
After the cheese bubbles and stretches,
We'll eat it all if Mum lets us!

After all that temptation,
It reaches its final destination,
It's on the table in front of me,
At last it's time for tea!

I ate it so fast,
It's a shame it didn't last,
I just love to feed my face,
With the chieftain of the pizza race!

Jenna Welsh (11)
Wallacestone Primary School, Falkirk

Cat Kisses

I wish I had a kitten
With white fur and eyes of blue.
Oh what fun I'd have with her
And someone to love too.

Jasmine Prentice (8)
Wallacestone Primary School, Falkirk

To A Pizza

As I walk into the kitchen
your smell makes me salivate
for now I know it's pizza tonight.
As my mum tells me to sit down
it's a wondrous sight.

Your cheese bubbles
as you sit on my plate
your crunchy sizzling chicken lying on top.
Your toppings are like coats
to keep you warm.

As I pick up my knife and cut you up
your aroma fills the room.
As I lift you up one by one,
the smell as I hold you up to my mouth.
Your golden yellow crusts glistening in the light.

As I take a bite
your juice runs down my chin like blood.
Your crunchy crusts breaking in my mouth, like bones.
It really feels like a race,
as I shove you in my face.

How long will it be
before I meet your
brothers and sisters?

Ross Jamieson (11)
Wallacestone Primary School, Falkirk

At My School

There are some cats that rip the mats at school
So I just think they are fools.
And that must be why they were silly
Especially the one who is called Billy.

Lewis Calder (9)
Wallacestone Primary School, Falkirk

Friends

My friend has hair so fine.
When I touch it it turns to red wine.
Eyes like diamonds.
pretty and fine
Sun shines down and they glisten all night.
Lips so red, like roses so bright
Thorns that grow on her head all night.
She makes me feel happy and light
She's like an angel all through the night
Making sure everything's right.

Helping people, caring too
So smart,
She is clever too.
If she helps me she'll help you too
Walking around not making a sound
When I'm sad she'll tell me not to go mad
if you need help she'll be by your side.

A star way up high in the silver sky,
Shining so bright like a light.
My friend is so kind, like a big ice cream.
I like my friend, so pretty and kind.

Lisa Corbett (10)
Wallacestone Primary School, Falkirk

The Spooky Cinema

Inside the cinema I heard a crash,
Then I heard a noise, it was a thrash.
That lead me right to a smash
Then this was just a mish-mash.

Then I heard a big clatter
Then I heard a pitter-patter.
It sounded like a window clatter
Then I thought it doesn't matter.

Craig Maxwell (9)
Wallacestone Primary School, Falkirk

My Hamster

My hamster is a monster,
He's brown and he sometimes frowns.
You wouldn't like to meet him
Mind you, I wouldn't like to keep him.
He twitches and he itches.
He's very squirmy too.
But his name is Hammy the hamster
And I wouldn't be parted from him.

Charlotte Bibby (8)
Wallacestone Primary School, Falkirk

Winnie The Pooh

Oh Winnie the Pooh how I love you,
You are the best and you will do.
Winnie the Pooh you are the best,
But sometimes you're a pest.
Oh Winnie the Pooh what is up with you?
You're always there right by my side,
If I am scared you're always around,
Sometimes you're even on the ground.
Oh Winnie the Pooh I love you.

Charley Hay (11)
Wallacestone Primary School, Falkirk

My Chinchilla

I have a chinchilla called Gizzy
And he runs round my feet and makes me dizzy.

He sleeps all day and eats all night
When I am in bed curled up tight.

His fur is like velvet, so soft to touch
My chinchilla Gizzy, I love him so much!

Callum Hill (8)
Wallacestone Primary School, Falkirk

Walking Through The Field One Day

Walking through the field one day,
A strange loud noise made me lose my way.
Just as the rain began to pour,
I heard the most enormous roar.
I slipped and fell into a bog
Then I saw it!
A big, black dog.
My heart thumped fast, up and down,
As the big, black dog towards me began to bound.
Now my heart began to race,
But all he did was lick my face!

Alisa Angus (8)
Wallacestone Primary School, Falkirk

To A Jelly

I just can't wait for Mum to say,
'Laura, the jelly is set and ready.'
I run into the kitchen and see,
Raspberry jelly saying, 'Eat me, eat me.'
I see you lying there.
I pick you up with my spoon.
I put you at the top of the tree.
You slither down the tree trunk like a snake.
You won't *stop* bouncing at the bottom.
I need more and more, eat and eat.
Now you are gone. Beware of another night.

Laura Gemmell (11)
Wallacestone Primary School, Falkirk